BIBLE

Student Edition • Grade 6

Colorado Springs, Colorado

Purposeful Design Publications is the publishing division of the Association of Christian Schools International (ACSI) and is committed to the ministry of Christian school education, to enable Christian educators and schools worldwide to effectively prepare students for life. As the publisher of textbooks, trade books, and other educational resources within ACSI, Purposeful Design Publications strives to produce biblically sound materials that reflect Christian scholarship and stewardship and that address the identified needs of Christian schools around the world.

Printed in the United States of America
19 18 17 16 15 3 4 5 6 7

Elementary Bible, grade 6
Purposeful Design Elementary Bible series
ISBN 978-1-58331-264-3 Student edition Catalog #10061

Purposeful Design Publications
A Division of ACSI
PO Box 65130 • Colorado Springs, CO 80962-5130
Customer Service: 800-367-0798 • www.purposefuldesign.com

Table of Contents

Name ____________________

God's Plan

1.1

Welcome to Sixth-Grade Bible!

This year, you will learn exciting lessons from God's Word. These lessons will help you study the New Testament and learn about the salvation through Jesus Christ. The New Testament shows the power of the Holy Spirit to enable Christians to live a life that pleases God and to share the gospel. Studying God's Word can help you grow in your relationship with God.

God had a plan for the world and its people even before He created it out of nothing!

1. Use the Glossary in the back of your textbook to write the definition of the words.

narrative: ____________________

meta: ____________________

2. The Bible is the big-picture narrative of God's plan for creating the world and relating to people. Use the Code Box to find out what God made each day of the Creation.

Day 1: _ _ _ _ _

Day 2: _ _ _ _ _ _ _ _ _

Day 3: _ _ _ _; _ _ _; _ _ _ _ _ _

Day 4: _ _ _; _ _ _ _ _; _ _ _ _ _

Day 5: _ _ _ _; _ _ _ _

Day 6: _ _ _ _ _ _ _; _ _ _ _ _ _

3. Read Genesis 3:1–15. Write one sentence telling what went wrong in the Garden of Eden. Then write one sentence telling the solution God foretold in verse 15.

____

____

____

____

1.2 God's Plan

1. Choose one of these Scripture passages to read. Then complete the news article on the basis of the information you have read. Be sure your article answers the questions, Who? What? Where? When? Why? and How?

   Gospel account: Luke 2:1–7
   Acts account: Acts 17:1–4 ("They" refers to Paul and his friends.)
   Epistle account: 2 Peter 1:1–8

THE
New Testament Chronicles

The Savior Revealed?

Some Jews are claiming that their Messiah, who has been foretold for centuries, has finally arrived!

____

____

____

____

____

____

____

____

____

____

____

____

____

____

____

____

____

____

____

2. Skim all the verses in Exercise 1. Draw a line from the Scripture reference to the phrase that describes what is happening in the passage.

Luke 2:1–7 •	• Jesus is proclaimed to people.
Acts 17:1–4 •	• Jesus is presented to people.
2 Peter 1:1–8 •	• Jesus is professed to people.

Name ____

God's Plan 1.3

A concordance is an index or a list of words or topics in the Bible and the verses that relate to them. Use these three sections of a concordance and your Bible to answer the questions or follow the directions.

1. Which two Scripture references in this concordance refer to a crown of life?

____

2. Which Bible reference tells what kind of life is the gift of God?

____

3. What kind of animal is Christ compared to in Isaiah 53:7?

____

4. Who takes away the sin of the world, according to John 1:29?

____

5. Fill in the blank: The eternal God is your

_______________________________________.

6. First Peter 1:19 is about the blood of Jesus. What animal's blood is it compared to?

____

7. What kind of crown did Jesus wear, according to the Gospel of John?

____

8. On whose head is a golden crown in the book of Revelation?

____

9. Look at the concordance entry for John 3:15 and write the opposite of having eternal life.

____

10. What kind of crown is a head with gray hair?

____

crown
Psalm 132:18 upon Himself His *c*
Proverbs 14:24 the *c* of the wise
Proverbs 16:31 head is a *c* of glory
John 19:5 *c* of thorns
Philippians 4:1 my joy and *c*
2 Timothy 4:8 *c* of righteousness
James 1:12 *c* of life
1 Peter 5:4 *c* of glory
Revelation 2:10 *c* of life
Revelation 3:11 no one may take your *c*
Revelation 14:14 on His head a golden *c*

eternal, or everlasting
Deuteronomy 33:27 *e* God is your refuge
Matthew 19:16 I do that I may have *e*
Mark 10:30 in the age to come, *e*
John 3:15 not perish but have *e*
John 6:47 believes in Me has *e*
Romans 6:23 the gift of God is *e*

lamb
Genesis 22:7 but where is the *l*
Isaiah 53:7 He was led as a *l*
1 Peter 1:19 of Christ, as of a *l*
Revelation 5:12 "Worthy is the *L*
Revelation 12:11 by the blood of the *L*

Lamb of God
John 1:29 the *L* of *G* who takes
John 1:36 "Behold, the *L* of *G*

1.4 God's Plan

As you complete this page, think about how the life story of a sixth grader can either fit within or not fit within the bigger narrative of God's Word and plan.

1. Read the sentences and decide whether to place their letter in the outer circle or the inner circle. The outer circle refers to God's Big Narrative. The inner circle refers to a life story of a sixth grader.

a. He reads his Bible and believes it is true.

b. It tells how the world was created and how it will end.

c. He talks kindly with his friends.

d. He tells his family about Jesus.

e. It is the most complete and important narrative ever told.

f. He goes to school to learn about the world God created.

g. It is divided into two main parts.

GOD'S BIG NARRATIVE

THE NARRATIVE OF A SIXTH GRADER'S LIFE

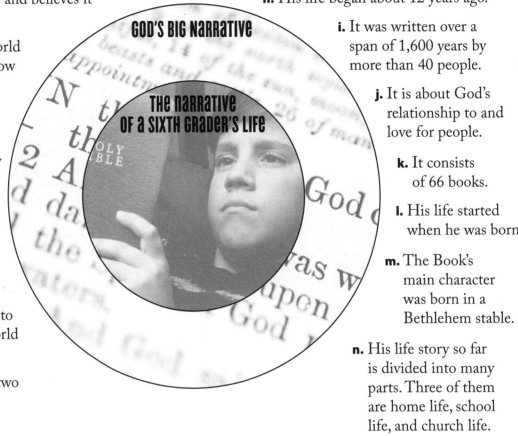

h. His life began about 12 years ago.

i. It was written over a span of 1,600 years by more than 40 people.

j. It is about God's relationship to and love for people.

k. It consists of 66 books.

l. His life started when he was born.

m. The Book's main character was born in a Bethlehem stable.

n. His life story so far is divided into many parts. Three of them are home life, school life, and church life.

2. Write a sentence that is true of the personal narrative of your own life.

____

3. How would you view the following if you wanted to fit into the big picture of God's plan?

a. God's Word? ______________________________

____

b. Jesus Christ? ______________________________

____

c. the plan of salvation? ______________________________

____

____

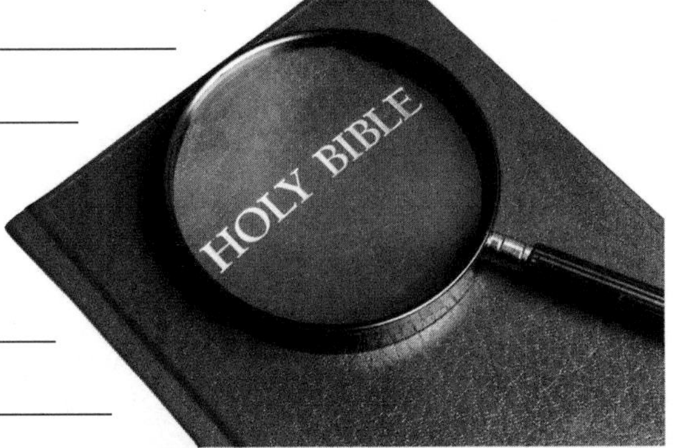

Name ____________________

Old Testament Overview

2.1

1. A redeemer is one who buys back or frees from captivity. From the passages, write on the lines who was redeemed. Then draw a picture in the boxes below to show how God redeemed each situation.

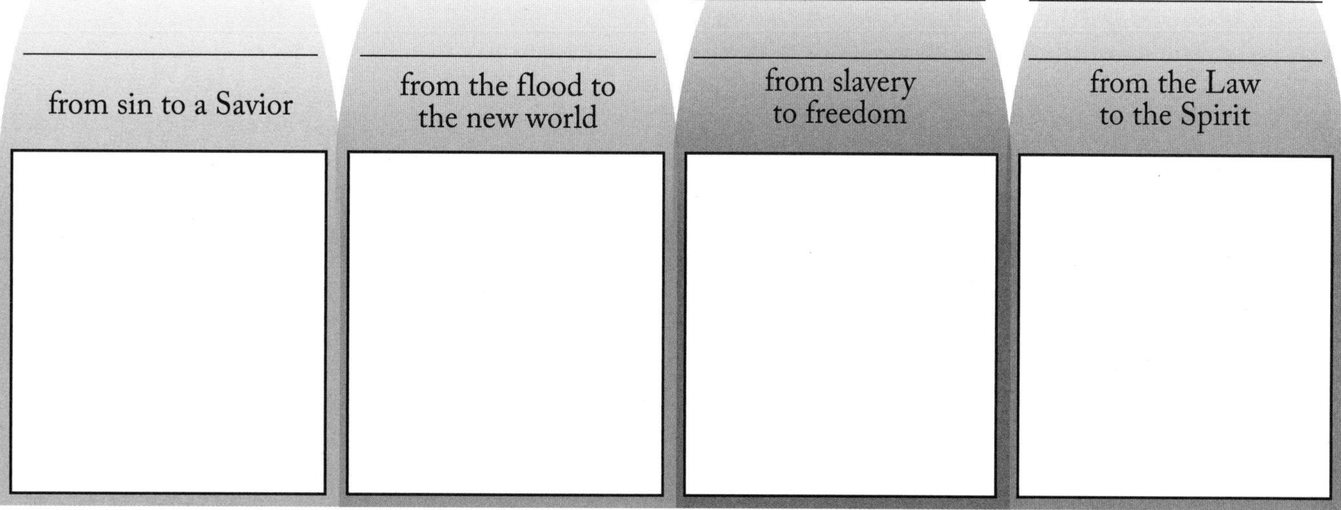

2. Read the story about the boy and his boat. Then answer the questions.

Twice Mine

A little boy decided to build a sailboat by himself. With loving care, he worked hard to carve the hull and make the sail. The boy painted the boat with his favorite colors. He carved his initials on the bottom of the hull. Finally, he took it to the lake to play one day. A storm suddenly came up, and the wind blew his boat out of reach and across the lake. The boy lost his boat. He searched for days but never found it. While walking home one day, the boy happened to see a sailboat for sale in a store window. He looked carefully to find his initials on the bottom of the hull. It was the very same boat, but this time it had a price tag on it. So the boy saved his money and bought his own boat. Walking home with the boat in his arms, the boy said, "You are twice mine, little boat. I made you, and I bought you back."

a. How was the boat the little boy owned twice his?

____

b. Read 1 Corinthians 6:19–20. How are believers twice Christ's?

____

____

3. What are you thankful for from God, the Redeemer?

____

____

2.2 Old Testament Overview

Complete the sentences about God's promises by filling in the letter lines next to the letters that match the letters of the missing words. The letters in the box reveal a word that means **promises**. This word is used in both the Old and New Testaments.

1. A __a__ covenant required a person to do something before God could respond.
2. The Old Testament covenants could be summarized by calling them the __b__ Covenant.
3. The covenant given to __c__ promised him an eternal throne in the line of the Messiah.
4. The covenants of the Old Testament could only __d__ sin temporarily through sacrifice.
5. The covenant through Jesus Christ will __e__ the effects of sin forever.
6. The covenant given to __f__ was to bless him with a family and to bless all nations through him.
7. Jesus Christ brought the __g__ Covenant, which allows people to change on the inside.
8. An __h__ covenant means that nothing is required of believers to gain the benefit of God's promises.
9. The covenant given to __i__ was that God would bless the children of Israel if they would obey the Ten Commandments.

Fill in the blanks and follow the directions.

10. The secret word is __ __ __ __ __ __ __ __ __. Use the Glossary at the end of this book to define it.

____

11. God started His plan of redemption with the Old Covenant. Define it by using the Glossary.

____

____

12. God still gives promises today. Write one of your favorite promises from the Bible and tell why it is your favorite.

____

____

Name ______________________________

Old Testament Overview 2.3

In the Old Testament, God's prophets declared truth to encourage the people to closely follow Him. Match the prophets with their message of restoration by writing the correct letter on the blanks.

Prophet	Message
___ **1.** Nathan (2 Samuel 12:7–13)	**a.** He persevered in warning rebellious Israel of coming judgment, though the nation did not return to God.
___ **2.** Elijah (1 Kings 18:21–40)	**b.** He directly spoke against sin in David's life. David repented and God restored him.
___ **3.** Jeremiah (Jeremiah 1:14–19)	**c.** He boldly confronted wicked Baal worship and evil rulers. The people honored God and killed the prophets of Baal.

God speaks today through His Word, through the Holy Spirit, and through godly people. But believers need to do more than just listen. Below are three reactions to God's truth. Use the Scriptures in the boxes to write a response to the comments. Be ready to share your advice in class.

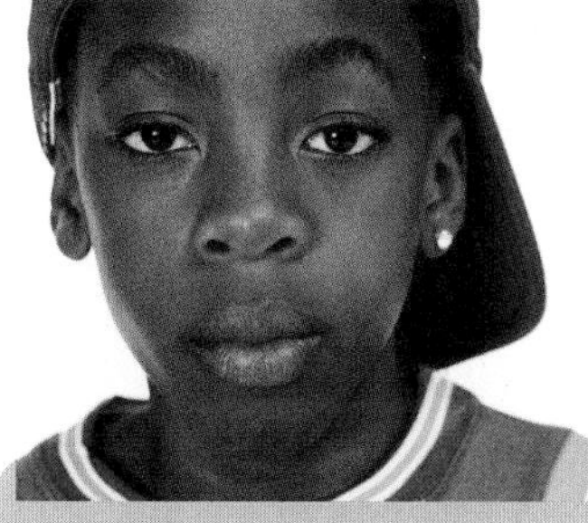

4. I go to church and try to listen in youth group. That's enough. I don't think I need to do anything about it.

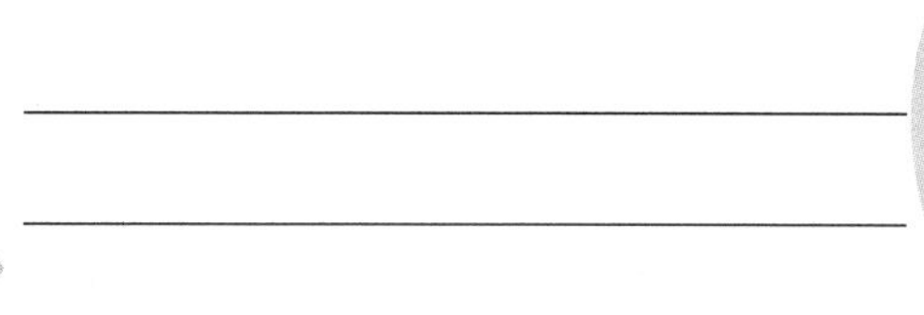

____
____
____
____
____

James 1:22 and 1:25

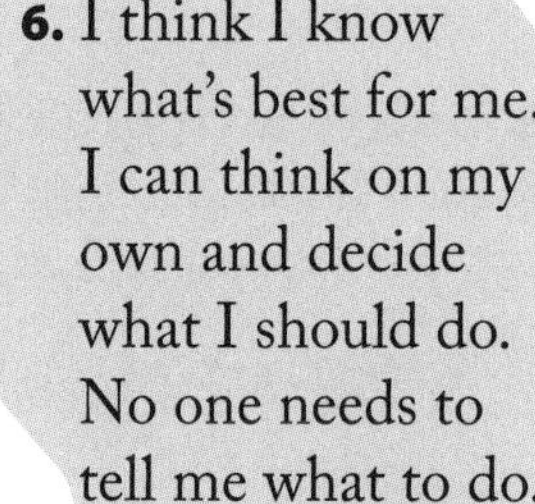

6. I think I know what's best for me. I can think on my own and decide what I should do. No one needs to tell me what to do.

____
____
____
____
____

Jeremiah 12:3

5. I look good on the outside, and I usually act nice. That's all that anyone can expect. Besides, no one knows what's going on inside my head or heart.

____
____
____
____
____

Psalm 139:23–24

2.4 Old Testament Overview

1. The Old Covenant in the Old Testament promised a savior who would fully restore people back to God. Though there are several categories of books in the Old Testament, nearly all of them mention this promise. Write the correct label from the Word Bank under the groups of Bible books.

Word Bank

- Poetry and Wisdom
- Minor Prophets
- Major Prophets
- OT History
- Law

____

____

____

____

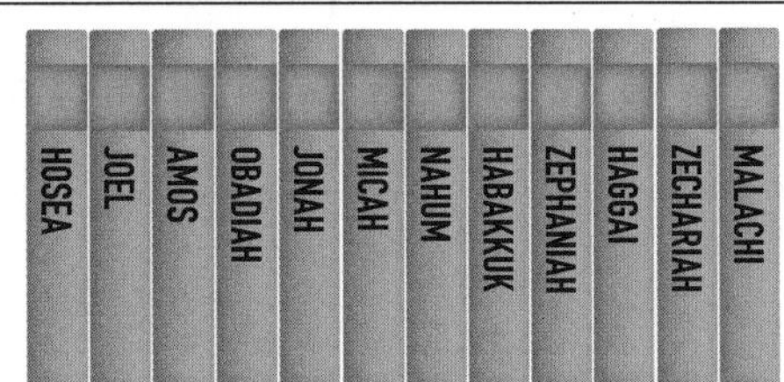

____

2. God's plan to redeem people is obvious in the Old Covenant. But this plan was not completed until the New Covenant was fulfilled through the Messiah. Identify the sentences below with **O** if a sentence refers to the Old Covenant, **N** if it refers to the New Covenant, and **B** if it refers to both.

___ Priests continually sacrifice animals.

___ God puts His law in people's mind and writes it on people's heart.

___ God gives His righteousness to those who believe.

___ Sin's effects are permanently canceled.

___ Sin is temporarily covered.

___ Jesus died once for all sins.

___ The Law demands total obedience.

3. What do you think is the best part for believers living under the New Covenant today compared to living under the Old Covenant back in Old Testament times?

____

____

4. Define justify using the Glossary in the back of your textbook.

____

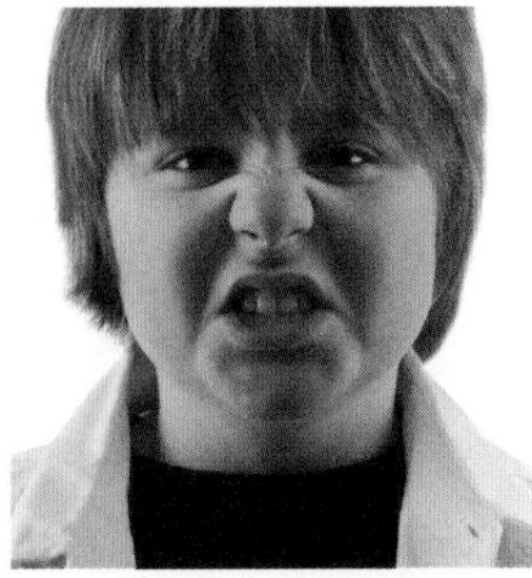

5. Give an example of a way that you or a Christian you know has been transformed or changed.

____

____

____

Name ______________________________

New Testament Overview 3.1

1. The Old Covenant revealed people's sin and inability to keep the Law. The New Covenant does not require people to do something to keep covenant. God has done everything! People simply accept Jesus. Read Exodus 20:3–17. In the box below, underline with a blue marker what the people were supposed to do. Then look up Jeremiah 31:31–34. Circle with a red marker what God promised to do.

make a new covenant
remember their sins no longer
honor God's name
put laws in their mind
keep God first in their life
honor their parents
write laws on their heart
worship only God
value human life
respect others' property
forgive their sins
feel content with what they have
honor marriage
keep the Sabbath holy
become their God
talk truthfully about their neighbor

Complete the sentences.

2. When the Israelites disobeyed, they were required to

______________________________.

3. When anyone wants to receive the New Covenant, he or she only needs to

______________________________.

Look up the Scriptures and unscramble the characteristics of the New Covenant as revealed in the New Testament. Write the correct characteristic on the lines.

4. Hebrews 9:15 ______________________________

laneret thraninceie

5. Romans 11:27 ______________________________

greesinfosv fo niss

6. 2 Corinthians 5:21 ______________________________

het strengsoihuse fo odG

7. 2 Corinthians 3:17 ______________, or ______________

byteril emodfer

8. 2 Corinthians 3:6 ______________________________

eilf viggin

9. 2 Corinthians 5:18 ______________________________

iclintoocainer

Answer the question in two or three complete sentences. Use Scriptures to support your points.

10. Why is it better for people to live under the New Covenant rather than the Old Covenant?

____

____

____

3.2 New Testament Overview

Match the Gospel writers (first column) to the way they presented Jesus (middle column). Then match their presentation of Jesus to its explanation (third column).

1. Mark •	• Messiah and King •	• Jesus understands people's weaknesses.
2. John •	• Servant and Redeemer •	• Jesus fulfilled prophecy, and He will reign forever.
3. Luke •	• Son of Man •	• Jesus has power over sin and death.
4. Matthew •	• Son of God •	• Jesus served and saved others.

The Gospels teach about Jesus. Read the descriptions below. Use the information above as clues for starting to look up each reference in the Gospels. Write the correct Gospel to complete the reference.

5. Jesus and the Father are one. (________________ 10:30)

6. Jesus wants the salvation message to be preached to all nations. (________________ 13:10)

7. Jesus was willing to suffer. (________________ 22:42)

8. Jesus amazed people with His teachings and miracles. (________________ 6:2)

9. Jesus foretold that He would spend three days and three nights buried. (________________ 12:40)

10. Jesus offers eternal life to anyone who will believe in Him. (________________ 6:47)

11. Jesus came to Earth to save lost people. (________________ 3:17)

12. Jesus is the only one who can forgive sins. (________________ 2:10)

Choose one Gospel writer and blog about Jesus in that author's style or to that author's audience. Then read the blog and have other students guess which author you chose.

13. ____

____

____

____

____

____

Name ______________________________

New Testament Overview

3.3

Be a detective and use the Scriptures to write details about each person or point on the time line. Some questions are provided to guide you in finding the important details in the passages.

Pentecost and the establishment of the Church	Stoning of Stephen	Paul's (Saul's) conversion on the road to Damascus
1. Holy Spirit	**2.** Stephen	**3.** Paul
Acts 2:1–4 What unusual thing appeared? ______	Acts 6:8 What is known about Stephen's actions? ______	Acts 9:1–2 Why was Saul on his way to Damascus? ______
Acts 2:5–8 What ability did the believers receive? ______	Acts 6:9–11 What was he accused of? ______	Acts 9:3–6 What did he encounter on the way? ______
Acts 2:41 What result came from Peter's bold preaching? ______	Acts 7:55 What did he see during his trial? ______	Acts 9:17–20 How did Saul respond to Ananias? ______
	Acts 7:58 Who was present at his stoning? ______	Acts 9:22–23 How did Jewish people react to Saul's transformation? ______

3.4 New Testament Overview

1. Write the name of each category of Bible books on the lines connected to the gold plates.

Word Bank

Prophecy
Gospels
Letters
History

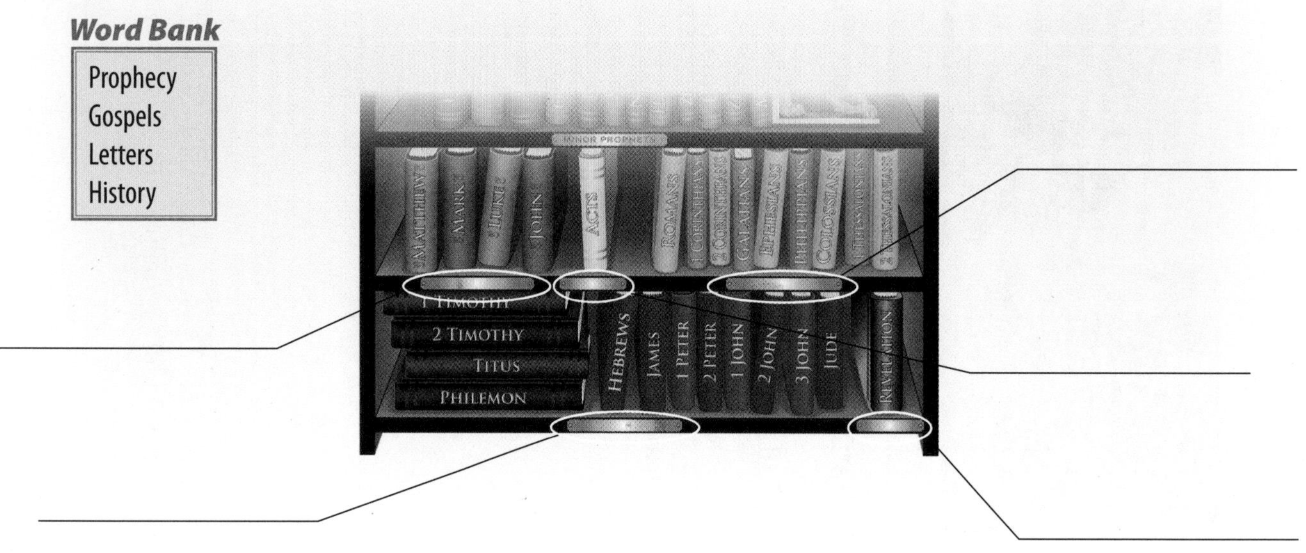

2. When a person says yes to salvation, reading the Bible helps the person learn more about God's ways. It helps him or her live a life that pleases God. Each Epistle contains characteristics of the abundant Christian life. An epistle is a letter. Write the number of the word that best fits the references in the boxes. Check your answers by adding up the numbers in each column. If the answers are correct, the sum for each row, column, and diagonal will be the same. Write the sum on the line.

1 faith in the Son of God
2 fellowship
3 peace
4 contentment
5 truth
6 self-control
7 doers of the word
8 faith sharing
9 endurance or perseverance
10 unity
11 joyfulness
12 generosity
13 righteousness
14 love
15 thankfulness
16 humility

____ Galatians 2:20	____ 1 Thessalonians 1:2	____ Colossians 3:14	____ 1 Timothy 6:6
____ 2 Corinthians 9:5	____ 2 Peter 1:6	____ James 1:22	____ Hebrews 12:1
____ Philemon 6	____ Ephesians 4:3	____ Philippians 4:4	____ 3 John 4
____ Romans 3:22	____ Jude 2	____ 1 John 1:7	____ 1 Peter 5:5

THE SUM IS ____.

Name ______________________________

A Look at Matthew

4.1

Read the statement in the center of the page and look up the verses in the surrounding spaces. Write each prophecy and its fulfillment that are found in the passages. Remember that God is omniscient and that He planned long before Jesus was born just how these prophecies would be fulfilled.

JESUS IS THE PROMISED MESSIAH OF THE KINGDOM OF HEAVEN.

1. Matthew 2:3–11
The wise men were looking for baby Jesus.

Prophecy: ______________________________

Fulfilled: ______________________________

2. Matthew 4:12–17
Jesus moved from Nazareth to Capernaum.

Prophecy: ______________________________

Fulfilled: ______________________________

3. Matthew 8:16–17
Jesus healed the sick.

Prophecy: ______________________________

Fulfilled: ______________________________

4. Matthew 12:15–21
Large crowds followed Jesus, and He healed the sick.

Prophecy: ______________________________

Fulfilled: ______________________________

5. Matthew 21:1–5
Jesus got ready to go into Jerusalem.

Prophecy: ______________________________

Fulfilled: ______________________________

6. Matthew 27:3–10
Judas threw down the silver coins of betrayal and killed himself.

Prophecy: ______________________________

Fulfilled: ______________________________

4.2 A Look at Matthew

How does what you value affect your choices? Read each scenario. In the first box to the side, write at least two values that would affect this decision. Then write in the second box the decision you think the person in each scenario should make.

1. Terryl is raising money to provide supplies for a school in the Democratic Republic of Congo. He knows that the school is very poor and that the teachers there teach about salvation through Jesus. So, he is trying to raise more money than anyone else in his class. But Terryl just found out that Aimee is $60 ahead of him. Also, he realizes that there is only one week left before the money is due. He thinks about putting in $80 from his savings account.

Value

Decision

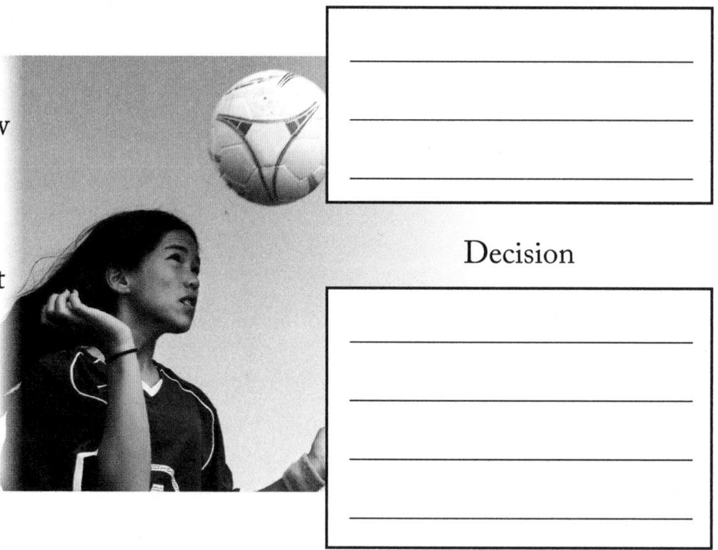

2. Ever since the second grade, Celeste and Jazi have loved watching movies together. But now Celeste likes to go shopping, while Jazi loves playing soccer. They have not spent time together for almost three months. Celeste is planning a special shopping trip with her aunt so they can get Celeste's mom a big birthday gift. Jazi calls and tells Celeste that she fell during a game and broke her foot. Jazi wants Celeste to watch movies together, but Celeste is not sure that she wants to.

Value

Decision

Read Matthew 6:24. Know that some Bible translations use **mammon** to refer to **a person's property or anything a person trusts in**. In one sentence, tell what the verse means. Then answer the question.

3. ______________________________

4. How can you guard against things in your life becoming mammon?

Name ____

A Look at Matthew 4.3

1. Read Matthew 6:19–21. Then unscramble the words from the passage and think about where your values are being stored. Note that no words are repeated.

2. Think about the above pictures. Which reminds you of something you might be tempted to make your main treasure instead of Jesus? ____

Take time to talk to God about valuing Jesus as your most important treasure.

3. Paraphrase Matthew 6:19–21 as if you are telling a friend what it says.

____

____

____

____

____

____

____

4.4 A Look at Matthew

1. How do you get from a value to a Christlike decision? Start at the three value words at the top and draw a line from each value to the related decision at the bottom of the exercise. Then, on each of your three lines, write an example that is based on a relationship with God and the value of His kingdom.

RELATIONSHIP STEWARDSHIP TRUST

I depend on God for what I need.	I use the gifts and talents God has given me to spread the Kingdom.	I spend time with God to know His ways.

2. Read Hebrews 13:5a. Explain how this verse applies to at least one of the values listed in Exercise 1 and to your life.

____

____

____

Name ______________________________

A Look at Mark 5.1

Biblical success means **knowing Christ and following Him through consistent obedience, faithful service, and mature growth.**

1. Read the Bible passages about the people listed. Decide, on the basis of the actions you read about, whether each person was a success or a failure in these instances. Place a check mark in the correct box. Then explain why in the Reason column.

Person	Success	Failure	Reason
Joseph (Genesis 39:20–23)			
Moses (Exodus 2:11–15)			
Hezekiah (2 Kings 18:1–7)			
Peter (Luke 22:54–62)			

2. Think of two people from the Bible, history, or your life who have been biblically successful. Write their name on the line and explain why you chose them.

Person	Success	Reason
______________	✓	
______________	✓	

5.2 A Look at Mark

The following list includes both heavenly and earthly treasures. On the lines, rewrite the list in order of importance. Find the most important treasure of all and write it for Exercise 1. The answers for the 2–4 group of heavenly treasures should come before the 5–8 group of earthly treasures. (Note: Just order them all from what you think is most important to what you think is least important.)

1. ____________________
2. ____________________
3. ____________________
4. ____________________
5. ____________________
6. ____________________
7. ____________________
8. ____________________

Being honest
Telling others about Jesus
Having money
Winning trophies
Being popular
Having a relationship with God
Gaining fame
Serving others

Jesus valued what His heavenly Father valued. He knew what biblical success meant. Read the godly truths Jesus demonstrated or taught. Then write one way you can follow His example. Be specific.

9. Jesus ate dinner with Matthew (also known as Levi), other tax collectors, and poor people. The Pharisees began to gossip about Jesus. But Jesus did not get embarrassed about being seen with these people. He desired to show everyone love and acceptance. He did not value success the same way the Pharisees did. (Mark 2:13–17)

I can follow Christ's example by ____________________

____________________.

10. A man went to Jesus to ask for healing for his daughter. A little while later, some people told him his daughter had died. Jesus encouraged the man to believe in God and taught him not to give in to fear. (Mark 5:35–36)

I can follow Christ's example by ____________________

____________________.

11. Peter, James, and John went with Jesus to the garden of Gethsemane before the Crucifixion. Jesus told them to pray. Later, when Jesus found them asleep, He taught them that they should pray so as not to fall into temptation. (Mark 14:37–38)

I can follow Christ's example by ____________________

____________________.

Name ____

A Look at Mark 5.3

Jesus submitted to God. His teachings and selfless actions showed His relationship to His Father and helped others grow in faith. Read the exercises and verses. Then write what His powerful actions show you about God. Also write how learning these traits of God helps you grow in your relationship with Him.

1. Jesus healed a blind and mute man. He told the man not to tell anyone about the miracle He had performed. Jesus did not perform miracles to gain recognition or fame. He loved the man and wanted to bring His Father glory. (Mark 7:31–37)

____

____

____

2. Jesus was teaching in a synagogue when a man with an unclean spirit confronted Him. Jesus commanded the spirit to be silent and to come out of the man. The people in the synagogue were all amazed at Jesus' power and authority. (Mark 1:21–28)

____

____

____

3. Jesus had been praying on a mountain. His disciples were in a boat in the middle of the sea, trying to row against a mighty wind. Jesus walked on the water in the middle of the night to reach them. When they first saw Him, they were terrified. He told them to have courage and not to be afraid. Then the wind stopped. (Mark 6:45–52)

____

____

____

Solve the math problems to identify the Equation for Success. The first three problems have words in them. First, write the number each word equals. Then, write each word above its matching number in the Equation for Success below. In the last three problems, a symbol is used. Place the matching number on the line above that symbol in the Equation for Success.

4.

0 + me = 365	me = ____
God + 0 = 759	God = ____
0 + 1 = others	others = ____
(76 + 2) + 39 = 76 + (✋ + 39)	✋ = ____
💧 + 537 = 540	💧 = ____
7 + (1 + ✺) = (3 + 2) + 4	✺ = ____

Equation for Success: ____________ (759) ____st (✺), ____________ (1) ____nd (✋), and ____________ (365) ____rd (💧)

5.4 A Look at Mark

These sentences give steps for success. Read the Bible verses. Cross out the wrong word or phrase in each sentence and replace it with a word or phrase from the verse to complete the secret. Write the new word or phrase on the line.

1. It will take more effort to chop with a dull ax. Instead of using more strength, joy will bring success. (Ecclesiastes 10:10) ____________

2. Be strong and very nice. Meditate on God's Word day and night so that you will be careful to do what it says. Do not stray and you will be prosperous and successful. (Joshua 1:7–8) ____________

3. While believers are on Earth, they are absent from Christ's glory. But they walk by the law and not by sight. Their aim is to be with God. (2 Corinthians 5:6–9) ____________

4. As long as King Uzziah sought after his own desires, he would prosper. (2 Chronicles 26:5) ____________

5. A righteous person delights in the law of the country and meditates on it day and night. (Psalm 1:2) ____________

Reread the steps for success listed above. Summarize each one in five words or less.

6. • ____________
   • ____________
   • ____________
   • ____________
   • ____________

How successful are you? Are you doing the things that lead to success? Do you seek the Lord's will and obey the Bible? Reread Joshua 1:8. Write one thing you will commit to do this week to be more biblically successful.

7. ____________
____

Name ______________________________

A Look at Luke 6.1

1. Explain the term Son of Man.

____

____

2. Use the word Gentile in a sentence to describe Luke.

____

____

3. Refer to the Summary of Luke's Gospel sheet to complete the outline.

I. The introduction of the Son of Man (Luke 1–3)

A. ______________________________

B. ______________________________

C. ______________________________

D. ______________________________

II. The ministry of the Son of Man (Luke 4–8)

A. ______________________________

B. ______________________________

III. The rejection of the Son of Man (Luke 9–11)

A. ______________________________

B. ______________________________

C. ______________________________

D. ______________________________

IV. The teachings of the Son of Man (Luke 12–19)

A. ______________________________

B. ______________________________

V. The death of the Son of Man (Luke 20–24)

A. ______________________________

B. ______________________________

C. ______________________________

D. ______________________________

6.2 A Look at Luke

1. Wherever He went, Jesus spent time with people whom few others appreciated. Read the verses from the Gospel of Luke. Write whom Jesus spent time with and what He did for each one.

Passage	Whom Jesus Met	What Jesus Did
7:37–38 and 7:48	______________	______________
8:2	______________	______________
15:1–2	______________	______________
17:12–14	______________	______________
23:39–43	______________	______________

2. Identify fruits of the Spirit that Jesus either exhibited or talked about in Luke 15:1–10. Find lost sheep and coins by circling the ones that contain fruits of the Spirit. (Hint: Use Galatians 5:22–26.)

Answer the questions.

3. Why did Jesus show such concern for seeking and saving the lost? ______________

____

4. Why should believers have this same concern for the lost? ______________

____

5. In what ways can believers put this concern for the lost into action? ______________

____

Name ______________________________

A Look at Luke

Refer to Luke 15:11–32. Find verses in this passage about the lost son that show the following characteristics. Write each reference and explain why you chose it. Then answer the question in Exercise 6.

1. love ______________________________

2. forgiveness ______________________________

3. humility ______________________________

4. kindness ______________________________

5. submission ______________________________

6. Why is the younger son in this parable referred to as **lost**? ______________________________

Jesus seeks relationships with people. He also wants believers to have good relationships with others. Read Ephesians 6:1–3 to find out what kind of relationship Jesus wants you to have with your parents.

7. Circle the words that describe the relationship children should have with their parents.

   obedient   rebellious   honoring   arguing   submissive

8. What is so special about the commandment in Ephesians 6:1? ______________________________

9. Why else is it important to do what your parents tell you to do? ______________________________

10. How well do you obey your parents? How can you improve in obeying them? ______________________________

11. Make an analogy between the commandment in Ephesians 6:1 and how you should act toward God as your heavenly Father. ______________________________

6.4 A Look at Luke

Do you want to get along with people in your life? Jesus gives advice on how. Read the verses in Luke and complete the sentences.

1. (6:31) Treat others as ______________________________.
2. (6:35) Love ______________________________.
3. (6:36) Be merciful ______________________________.
4. (6:37) Do not judge and ______________________________.
5. (6:37) Do not condemn and ______________________________.
6. (6:37) Forgive and ______________________________.
7. (6:38) Give and ______________________________.

Think of the last time you were unkind. Why were you unkind? Sometimes people are unkind to make themselves look good. Read what Jesus had to say about this in Luke 6:41–42. Complete the sentences.

8. The speck represents ______________________________.
9. The plank or beam represents ______________________________.
10. The verses are telling me to ______________________________

    ____

    ______________________________.

Read the situations below and answer the questions.

11. The boy who sits in front of you keeps taking your pencils and saying they are his. Then he laughs at you and calls you names when you tell the teacher. What should you do?

    ____

    ____

    ____

12. The new girl at school has been spreading rumors about you. They are not true, but now even your good friends are starting to avoid you. You see the new girl alone after school, and she is laughing at you. What should you decide to do?

    ____

    ____

13. Your brother leaves dirty clothes all over your room. You have asked and asked, but he still will not pick them up. What should you do?

    ____

    ____

Name ____

A Look at John

Look up the verses. Read the verses before and after reading the descriptions. Decide who is declaring that Jesus is the Son of God. Write the letter of the reference in front of its matching description. Then write the person's name or title under the matching description on the left.

___ **1.** Jesus saw him sitting under a fig tree. ______________________	**a.** JOHN 1:34–36
___ **2.** He came before Jesus to prepare the way and baptized people. ______________________	**b.** MARK 1:1
___ **3.** He was a leader among the disciples. ______________________	**c.** LUKE 1:26–31
___ **4.** He was not one of the first 12 disciples, but he wrote the second Gospel. ______________________	**d.** MATTHEW 27:54
___ **5.** He was a Roman who saw Jesus die. ______________________	**e.** JOHN 1:48–50
___ **6.** He was a heavenly being who brought good news to Mary. ______________________	**f.** JOHN 6:68–69

Write complete sentences to answer the questions.

7. Why is it important for people to understand the Incarnation and believe that Jesus is God's Son?

____

____

____

8. Read John 20:31. What was John's purpose in writing his Gospel? List both reasons and include both names of Jesus that are noted in the verse.

a. ____

____

b. ____

____

7.2 A Look at John

1. The Holy Spirit has many names. Use the verses, the arrows, and the colored lines to find some of those names. Write a name on each line. (Bible translations sometimes vary when naming the Holy Spirit.)

2. The disciples were afraid because Jesus was going away. He comforted them with a promise of the indwelling Holy Spirit. Read John 14:16–19 and circle only the accurate phrases below.

The disciples would not be alone.
The Father will send the Holy Spirit.
Everyone will see and know the Spirit.
The Helper will come for a while.
The Spirit will not lie.
The Father answers the Son's prayers.

3. The Holy Spirit is a gift to believers. Use the words in the gift box to fill in the letter boxes.

The Holy Spirit is a wonderful ☐☐☐☐ from God the ☐☐☐☐☐☐! How much He must ☐☐☐☐ those who accept His Son as Savior to give them such a gift. Now they will always have someone who can ☐☐☐☐☐☐☐☐☐☐ and ☐☐☐☐☐☐☐ them. He will never ☐☐☐☐☐ them.

LOVE
FATHER
LEAVE
GIFT
UNDERSTAND
COMFORT

Name ____________________

A Look at John 7.3

Each box contains a code to represent a New Testament Bible verse.

- The first number tells you which book to look in.
- The second number tells you the chapter.
- The third number tells you the verse.

For instance, 4 3 16 would be John 3:16.

Use your Bible to write the reference and a word or a phrase that tells what the Holy Spirit's work is.

3 12 12	1. ____________________
6 8 26	2. ____________________
4 16 13	3. ____________________
6 8 2	4. ____________________
7 3 16	5. ____________________
9 5 22	6. ____________________
10 2 18	7. ____________________
23 4 13	8. ____________________
5 9 31	9. ____________________
6 8 1	10. ____________________
7 12 4	11. ____________________

The Holy Spirit comforts and counsels believers, but He also convicts or convinces unbelievers about three errors in belief. Refer to John 16:7–11 and complete the statements.

12. Unbelievers are guilty of ____________ because they do not ____________ Jesus is the Son of God.

13. ____________ does not come from doing everything right, but from God.

Jesus went to the ____________.

14. Unbelievers are wrong about ____________ because they believe the lies of ____________.

7.4 A Look at John

Show responses you can make to the way the Holy Spirit works. Complete the sentences by writing the correct letter on the lines in the triangles.

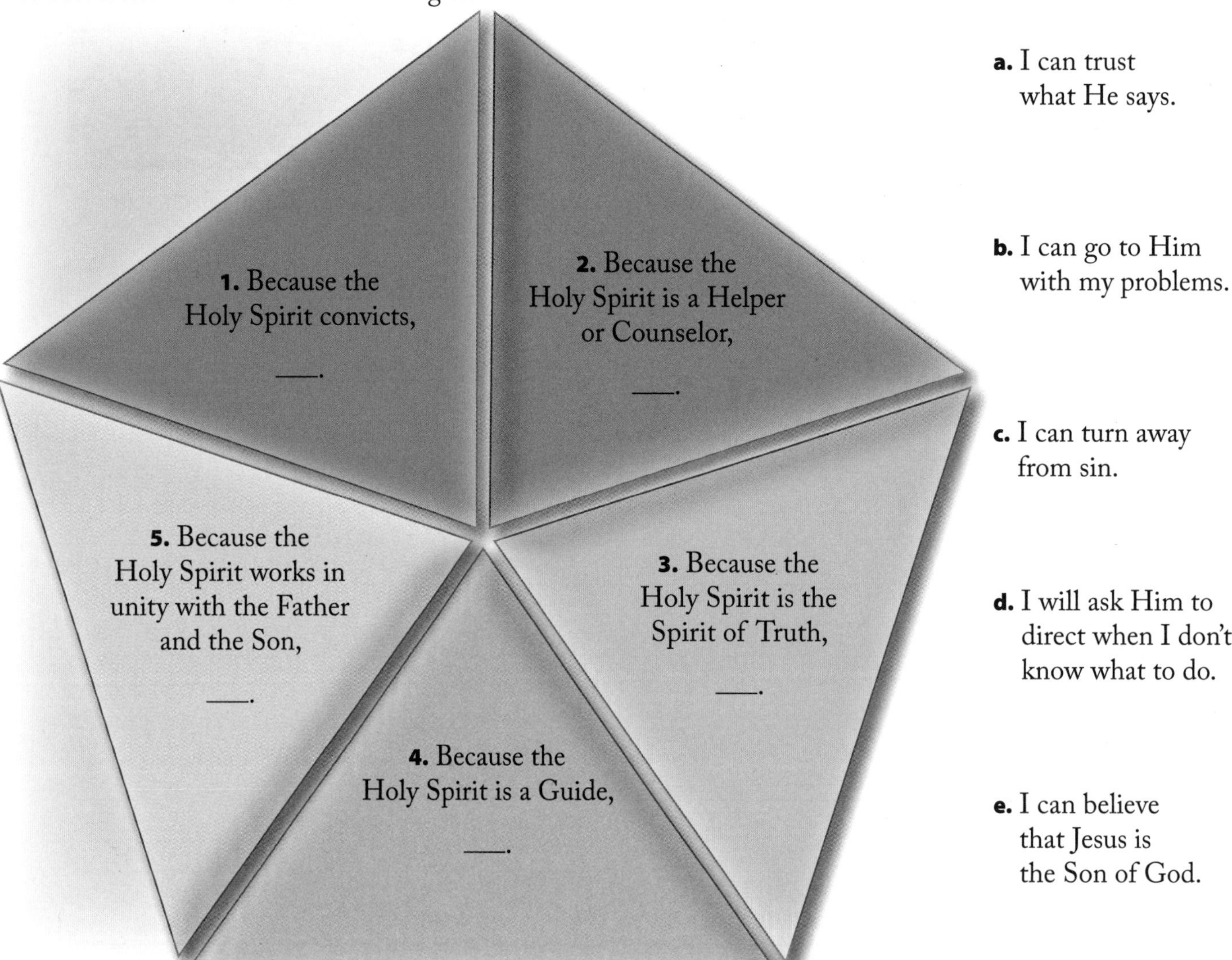

1. Because the Holy Spirit convicts, ___.
2. Because the Holy Spirit is a Helper or Counselor, ___.
3. Because the Holy Spirit is the Spirit of Truth, ___.
4. Because the Holy Spirit is a Guide, ___.
5. Because the Holy Spirit works in unity with the Father and the Son, ___.

a. I can trust what He says.

b. I can go to Him with my problems.

c. I can turn away from sin.

d. I will ask Him to direct when I don't know what to do.

e. I can believe that Jesus is the Son of God.

The Holy Spirit is more than a power or a force. He is one of the three Persons of the Trinity. Have you ever spoken to the Holy Spirit as a Person? Write a letter that expresses gratitude for the way the Holy Spirit works in a believer's life.

6. Dear Holy Spirit,

____

____

____

____

____

____

____

Name ____________________

Acts: The Early Church

8.1

The New Testament records 10 times when Jesus appeared after His resurrection. Look up each Scripture and write who saw Him. Then answer the question.

1. Matthew 28:5–10 ____________________
2. Mark 16:9–11 ____________________
3. Mark 16:14 ____________________
4. Luke 24:13–15 ____________________
5. Luke 24:33–34 ____________________
6. Luke 24:36–43 ____________________
7. John 20:24–29 ____________________
8. John 21:1–2, Mark 10:35 ____________________
9. 1 Corinthians 15:6 ____________________
10. 1 Corinthians 15:7 ____________________
11. Why was it important for the New Testament to record that over 500 people saw Jesus alive after His death on a cross?

____

____

Acts 1:8 records Jesus' mandate to evangelize the world. Jesus told the disciples to start in Jerusalem and move outward to Judea, Samaria, and to the end of the earth. Personalize Acts 1:8 by filling in the blanks.

12. Jerusalem = my city ____________________
13. Judea = my state or region ____________________
14. Samaria = neighboring state or region ____________________
15. End of the earth = farthest place from where I live ____________________

8.2 Acts: The Early Church

Twelve apostles are listed in Acts 1, but others were mentioned later in the New Testament. Look up the Scriptures and name the other apostles.

1. Acts 14:14 ______________________________

2. Galatians 1:19 ______________________________

Jesus gave a mandate to His followers to preach the gospel everywhere. The apostles began the job, but this mandate is yet to be completed. Look at the map to see where the apostles took the gospel. Cross out every other letter (starting with the second letter in each word) to see at least one of the places that each apostle went according to church tradition. Then write the number of the apostle in the shaded circle next to the matching area.

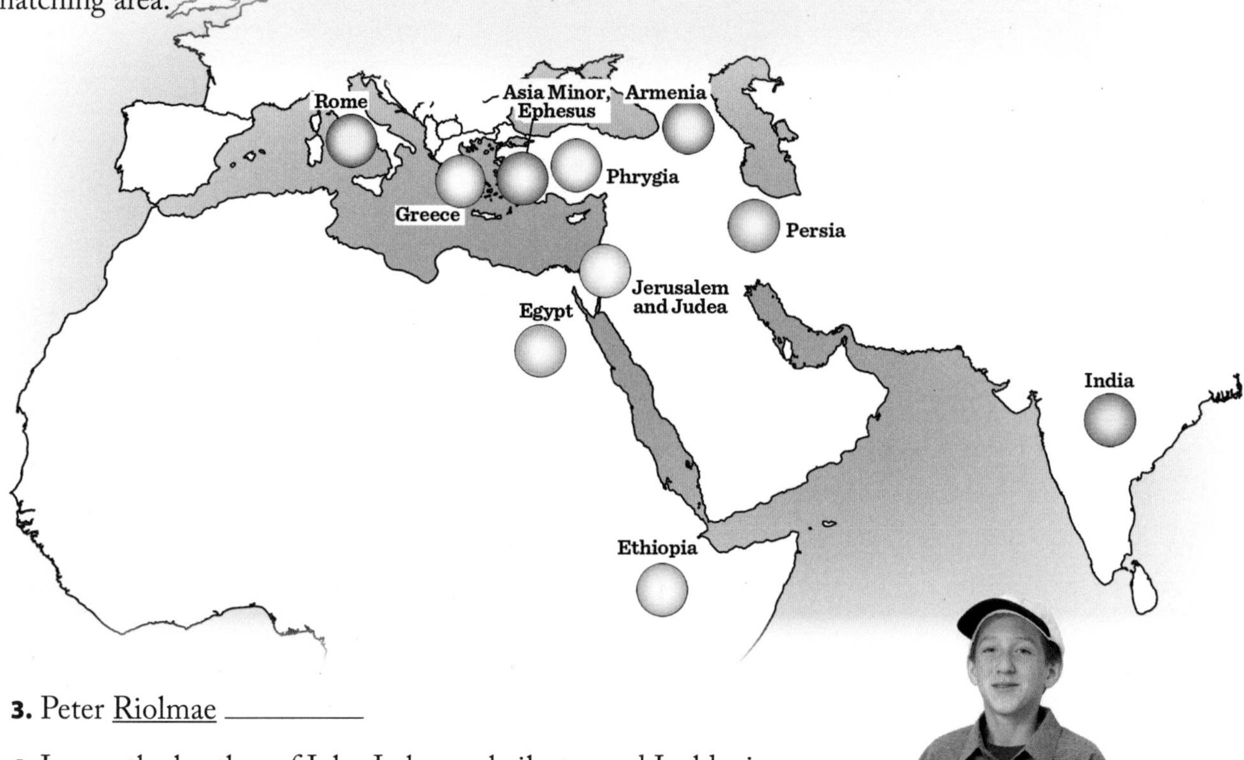

3. Peter Riolmae __________

4. James, the brother of John Jrebrxunshailsetm and Jauldoeia

____

5. John Atshina Mzivnyowr, Ekpuhqebsjuts (Turkey)

____

6. Andrew Gardelescie ______________

7. Philip Psharayaghira (Turkey) ______________

8. Bartholomew Apramnefnxiya ______________

9. Matthew Ectehsinodphiua ______________

10. Thomas Imnedrisa ______________

11. James Ekgbyeput ______________

12. Thaddaeus Prezrmsyifa ______________

Name ______________________________

Acts: The Early Church

8.3

1. Imagine that you are a news reporter covering the day described in Acts 2:1–13. Write a news report by using the following prompts: Who? What? When? Where? Be sure to include an answer to the question in verse 12.

____

____

____

____

____

____

____

2. The Holy Spirit is God's gift to each believer in Jesus Christ. Look up the Scriptures and write the name of the person or group who received this gift.

3. God sent the Holy Spirit to the Jewish believers first and then to the Gentile believers. Read Acts 5:32. Who does God give the Holy Spirit to now?

____

8.4 Acts: The Early Church

1. The Holy Spirit's power made a difference in Peter's life. Refer to the Scriptures to fill in the blanks to show the change in Peter.

BEFORE PENTECOST	AFTER THE HOLY SPIRIT CAME
Peter would not even say he knew Christ. (John 18:17)	• Acts 2:14 and 2:22–24 __________ __________
He did not know where Jesus was going. (John 13:36)	• Acts 2:32–36 __________ __________
He was afraid and ran from the Roman soldiers. (Mark 14:50)	• Acts 2:38–40 __________ __________

2. The Holy Spirit's power can make a difference in every believer's life. Use Acts 2:42–47 and record the characteristics of the Church in Acts 2.

- __________
- __________
- __________
- __________
- __________
- __________

3. Look at the above list from Acts 2 and circle each activity that your church also does.

4. Write four ways your church is different from the Church of Acts 2.

- __________
- __________
- __________
- __________

5. Write a prayer asking the Holy Spirit's power to be seen in your class.

____

____

____

Name ____

Acts: Peter, Stephen, and Philip

9.1

1. Follow the growth of the early Church by plotting the number of believers recorded in each verse. Then, connect the dots to form a line graph. Also, draw a flame on the dot that represents which group of believers was the group to whom God first sent the Holy Spirit.

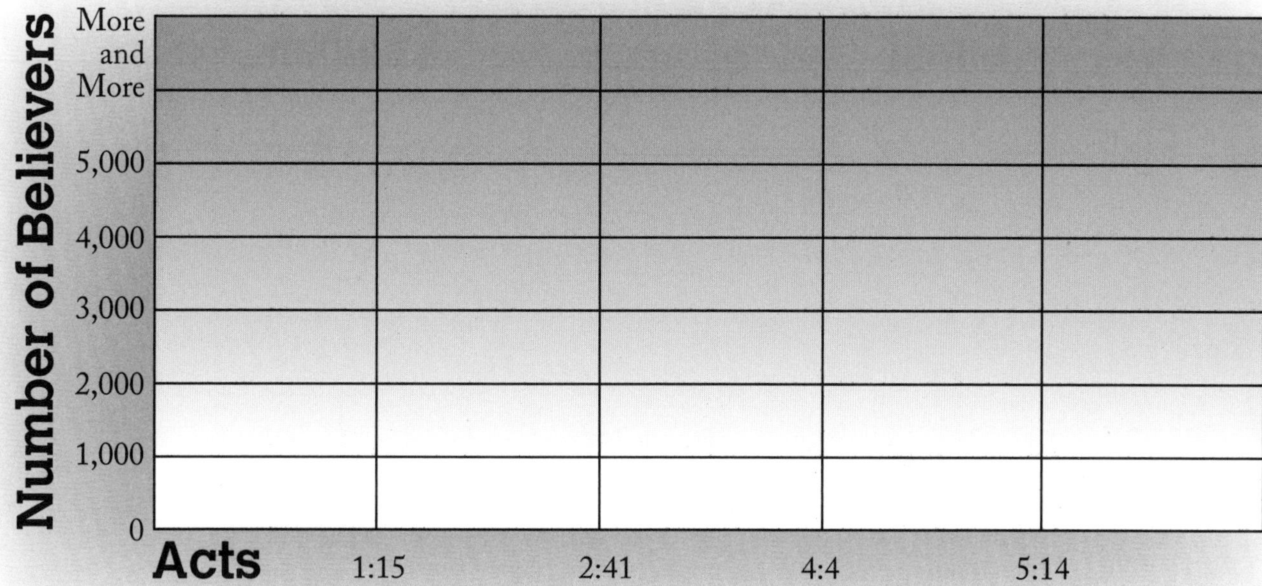

2. The Bible tells of many humanly impossible situations made possible through God's power! God uses ordinary people to do extraordinary things! Fill in the chart to show how God showed His power.

WHO?	WHAT WAS THE IMPOSSIBLE SITUATION?	WHAT DID GOD DO?
a. Genesis 37:28 ______________	Genesis 37:28 ______________ ______________	Genesis 45:5 ______________ ______________
b. Judges 6:13–16 ______________	Judges 7:16 ______________ ______________	Judges 8:22 ______________ ______________
c. Acts 5:34–37 ______________	Acts 5:29–33 ______________ ______________	Acts 5:38–40 ______________ ______________
d. Acts 9:32 ______________	Acts 9:33 ______________ ______________	Acts 9:34 ______________ ______________

9.2 Acts: Peter, Stephen, and Philip

Stephen experienced persecution from the Jewish religious leaders. He became the first Christian martyr. Look up the Scriptures. Then write the similarities between the death of Jesus Christ and the death of Stephen, a follower of Jesus.

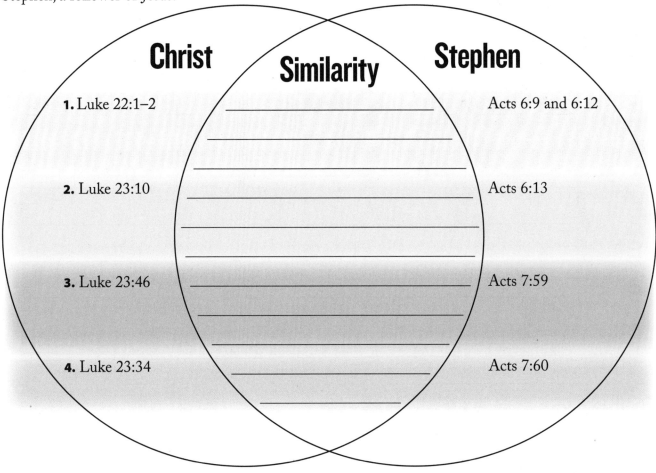

Christ	Similarity	Stephen
1. Luke 22:1–2		Acts 6:9 and 6:12
2. Luke 23:10		Acts 6:13
3. Luke 23:46		Acts 7:59
4. Luke 23:34		Acts 7:60

Tell how the person in the picture might be facing harassment or persecution for believing in Jesus. Then write a prayer for all Christians who face harassment or persecution.

5. Harassment:

Prayer:

6.

Persecution:

Prayer:

Name ____________________

Acts: Peter, Stephen, and Philip

9.3

Philip was an evangelist who traveled wherever God led him. God speaks and guides people in many ways. Look up the Scriptures and fill in the missing consonants to discover some ways God leads people.

1. PSALM 119:11 — by God's __ o __ __
2. Acts 13:2 — by __ __ e __ o __ __ __ __ i __ i __
3. Psalm 16:7 — by t __ __ __ or __'s __ ou __ __ e __
4. Acts 9:4–5 — by __ __ e __ oi __ __ o __ __ e __ u __
5. MATTHEW 1:20 — by __ __ ea __ __
6. Luke 1:26 — by a __ a __ __ e __

Follow the directions.

7. Name three places where you would like to go to evangelize people. Explain why.

____

____

____

8. Name three places where you would find it difficult to go to evangelize people. Explain why.

____

____

____

9. Sometimes it is difficult to share the gospel with others. But Scriptures can provide encouragement to share it. Choose one or more of the Scriptures to write yourself or someone else an encouraging note: Psalm 46:1–3 and 55:22, Isaiah 41:10, John 16:33, and 1 Peter 5:7.

9.4 Acts: Peter, Stephen, and Philip

1. Peter's vision showed some unclean animals that God ordered Peter to kill and eat. Look up these verses to discover what these animals were: Leviticus 11:4–7, 11:10, 11:13, and 11:29. Draw some of the animals that Jewish people were not allowed to eat, according to their laws.

2. After Peter's vision, he changed in the way he treated Gentiles. The apostles and some other believers in Judea criticized Peter for spending time with Gentiles. Peter went to Jerusalem to explain to these Jewish believers his vision and the trip to Cornelius' house. He told the apostles and other Jewish believers that the Gentiles had received the Holy Spirit. Read Acts 11:17–18. Then write at least one sentence to summarize the reaction of the Jewish believers.

____

____

____

____

Name ______________________________

Acts: Paul's Missionary Journeys

10.1

1. Use Acts 9:1–8 to fill in the speech balloons and to explain how the experience Saul had on the road to Damascus led to his conversion.

2. His life experiences helped Saul share the gospel with not only Jews but Gentiles and kings (Acts 9:15). Do the math problems. Circle each correct answer to the math problems along with the characteristic or ability that was useful to Paul in sharing the gospel.

a. (10 × 6) ÷ 5 + 16 = 28 Roman citizen / 30 great singing voice
b. (14 + 7) × 3 − 48 = 14 healthy / 15 well educated
c. ((69 ÷ 3) − 19) × 18 = 72 leader among the Jews / 74 physically strong
d. (55 × 3) ÷ 5 − 17 = 16 did not give up easily / 17 parents had a nice home
e. (9 × 14) ÷ 6 + 18 = 38 rich / 39 willing to obey
f. (24 × 4) ÷ 8 + 39 = 50 attended church regularly / 51 humble before the Lord
g. (67 − 43) × 7 ÷ 4 = 42 spoke boldly / 48 good cook

3. Think about your own life. What are some of your unique life situations or experiences? List three and then explain how you could use them to share the gospel with someone.

a. ______________________________

____

b. ______________________________

____

c. ______________________________

____

10.2 Acts: Paul's Missionary Journeys

Paul showed his commitment to Jesus before he began his missionary journeys. Look up the Scriptures and read them. Then write on the lines the place where Paul ministered.

1. Paul preached to the Jewish people in ________________. (Acts 9:20–22)
2. Paul spoke boldly about Jesus in ________________. (Acts 9:28–29)
3. Paul received revelation from Jesus when he went to ____________. (Galatians 1:12 and 1:17)
4. Paul taught the Gentile believers in ______________. (Acts 11:25–26)
5. Paul and Barnabas delivered an offering to believers in ____________. (Acts 11:28–30)

Read the scenarios and explain how the people could use their experience as an opportunity to share the gospel with others.

6. Shira takes music lessons and likes to write songs.

7. Alec won the Best Athlete Award at his Christian school.

8. Marcos uses a computer program to learn Chinese.

9. Kristen volunteers at a nursing home.

Name ____________________

Acts: Paul's Missionary Journeys

10.3

Imagine that you are Paul. Then use first-person pronouns and verbs to fill in each section of Paul's scrapbook page. (This means to write as if you are Paul.)

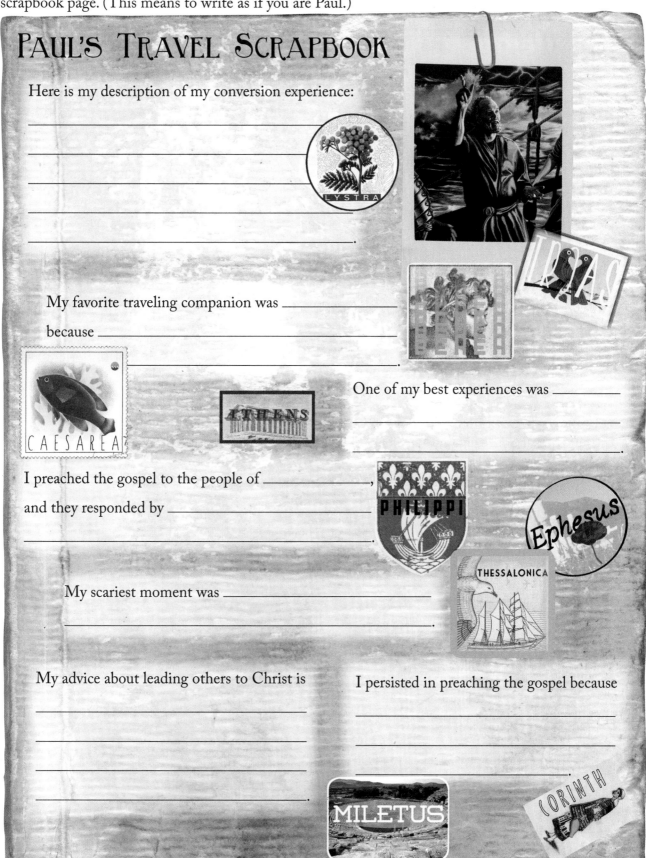

Paul's Travel Scrapbook

Here is my description of my conversion experience:

____

____

____

____

____________________.

LYSTRA

TROAS

BEREA

My favorite traveling companion was ____________________

because ____________________

____________________.

CAESAREA

ATHENS

One of my best experiences was ____________________

____

____________________.

I preached the gospel to the people of ____________________,

and they responded by ____________________

____________________.

PHILIPPI

Ephesus

THESSALONICA

My scariest moment was ____________________

____________________.

My advice about leading others to Christ is

____

____

____

____________________.

I persisted in preaching the gospel because

____

____

____________________.

MILETUS

CORINTH

10.4 Acts: Paul's Missionary Journeys

Use the book of Acts to complete this crossword puzzle containing the names of places that Paul visited.

Paul began all three missionary journeys from **1** (Acts 13:1). Paul traveled across to the island of **2** (13:4). Next he traveled up to **3** (13:13). Then he traveled to **4** Antioch (13:14), **5** (13:51), **6** (14:6), and **7** (14:6). Paul reversed the route and returned to **1**.

On the second journey, Paul traveled overland to the city of his birth **8** (9:11), and revisited **7**, **6**, and **5**. The Holy Spirit stopped him from going to Asia, so he went to **9** (16:8–9). There, he had a vision of a man calling from Macedonia. Paul obeyed and evangelized in **10** (16:12), where Paul and Silas were put in prison, and **11** (17:1), where an angry mob caused an uproar. Next, he arrived at **12** (17:10), where people received the Word gladly. Coming to **13** (17:15), he explained that their "unknown god" was Jesus Christ. **14** (18:1) was another stop before he headed to **15** (18:19) on his way back to **1**.

Traveling across land, Paul returned to encourage and strengthen the churches at **8**, **7**, **6**, **5**, **4**, and **15**. Next, he traveled across Macedonia down to Cenchrea before returning back to **9**, where a young man who had gone to sleep fell from a window. In **16** (20:15), Paul knew that he would be put in prison in **17** (21:15). But, Paul submitted because he knew this was God's will. He traveled to **18** (21:8) and then arrived in **17**.

After being captured, he appealed to the emperor and began another journey. While at **19** (27:8) on the island of **20** (27:7), Paul warned of upcoming disaster at sea. The captain ignored him, but after 14 days in a storm, the ship wrecked near the island of **21** (28:1). After three months, the ship sailed to its destination of **22** (28:16).

Name ________________________________

Romans: All Have Sinned 11.1

1. Define theology. ________________________________

2. Define doctrine. ________________________________

3. Paul's life dramatically changed when he personally met Jesus on the road to Damascus. His conversion created new convictions about God. Place an X on either the left or right side to identify the phrases as describing his life either before or after he became a Christian. Use the Scripture references as needed.

BEFORE

Philippians 3:4–8

2 Corinthians 11:21–28

2 Timothy 1:12

Romans 1:16–17

AFTER

__ counted his past gains or profits as losses __

__ was beaten many times by the Jews __

__ was zealous in persecuting the Church __

__ considered everything except Christ to be rubbish __

__ emphasized his strong Jewish heritage as a proud Pharisee __

__ suffered for the gospel but was confident of God's keeping power __

__ was blameless or faultless in obeying Jewish rules and keeping the Law __

__ was confident in the flesh—his own accomplishments __

__ was in danger from nature, the Gentiles, and the Jews __

__ was not ashamed of the power of the gospel of Christ __

4. Read 2 Timothy 1:12 and Romans 1:16. Why was Paul so unashamed of his new conviction about the power of God for salvation? ________________________________

____

____

5. Why are believers sometimes afraid to speak up with boldness about their faith?

____

____

6. Who do you know that needs Jesus? ____________ Take time right now to pray for opportunities to share your faith with that person. Pray that he or she would respond to God.

11.2 Romans: All Have Sinned

God has revealed Himself in people's conscience and in His creation. But many people do not notice or respond to His invitation for a personal relationship. Paul explained that instead of responding many people trade the value of knowing Him for worthless things. Use Romans 1 to fill in the missing words.

1. People think they are ________________ ... but become ________________. (1:22)

2. People exchange God's ________________ ... for idols. (1:23)

3. They exchange the ________________ of God ... for a ________________. (1:25)

Number the following phrases in order of their importance to you. Let number **1** be your top priority and number **5** your lowest. Write the number in the circles.

4.

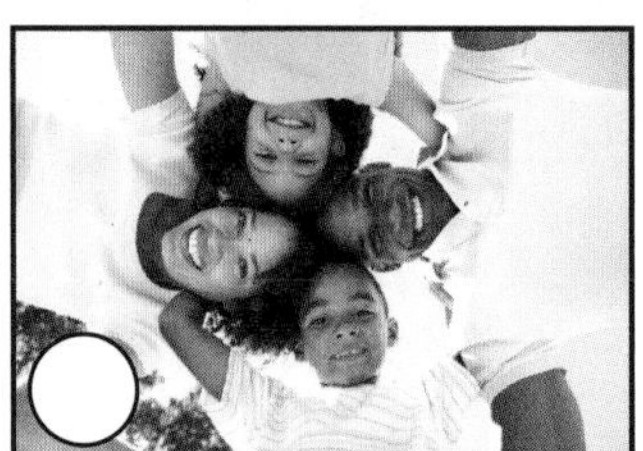

my family

my health and physical abilities

my things or possessions

my friends

my relationship to God

Follow the directions and answer the questions.

5. Briefly describe why you chose the priorities above. ________________________________

____

____

6. Why do you think some people would exchange valuable priorities for something less important?

____

____

7. What things might people choose as more valuable than a relationship with God?

____

____

Name ______________________________

Romans: All Have Sinned 11.3

The benefits of righteousness are listed in Romans 5:1–11. These benefits are realized to some extent soon after salvation. But they get better and better as a Christian grows in faith and maturity. Satan hates this realization and would try to deceive you into thinking the benefits are not that valuable. Follow the directions.

1. There are immediate benefits to following Jesus. Using Romans 5:1–3, circle the four internal benefits a new believer receives.

access to God by grace	easier life	hope of God's glory	joy even in difficulties
no troubles	happy all the time	peace with God	freedom from worry

2. Growth is another benefit. All Christians should grow to be more like Christ. Use the Word Bank on the right to list the growth sequence that occurs according to Romans 5:3–5a. Start at the bottom step.

Word Bank

hope
tribulation or suffering
no disappointment in hope
perseverance
character

3. Because God is at work in believers, things do change, from the inside out. Listed below are the changes. Look up the verses to understand these changes. Write the correct letter on the lines to match the type of change on the left to the explanation on the right.

___ My attitudes change. (Romans 5:1–3a, Philippians 2:3–5)

___ My character changes. (Romans 5:3b–5a, James 1:2–4)

___ My emotions change. (Romans 5:5b–8, Philippians 4:6–7)

___ My future changes. (Romans 5:9, Jeremiah 29:11)

___ My primary relationship changes. (Romans 5:10–11, 1 Corinthians 6:19–20)

a. God is omniscient and omnipotent. He knows you and has planned a hopeful future for you.

b. Your attitude should be the same as Christ's as you look out for the interests of others with humility and selflessness.

c. As a believer, the Holy Spirit is in you. This new relationship with Him changes everything. Now you honor God in all your life.

d. Now you talk to God about everything. You thank Him too, and His peace guards your heart (emotions) and mind (thinking) like never before.

e. You now face trials with a positive outlook. You know that these trials will produce maturity in you and complete your character.

11.4 *Romans: All Have Sinned*

Paul uses building blocks of faith to show believers how grace brings victory over sin. Start at the bottom of this page, where you see foundational truths. Then continue upward to understand Paul's teachings from Romans 6:1–23. Use the Scriptures to complete the fortress of faith as you build up by filling in blanks.

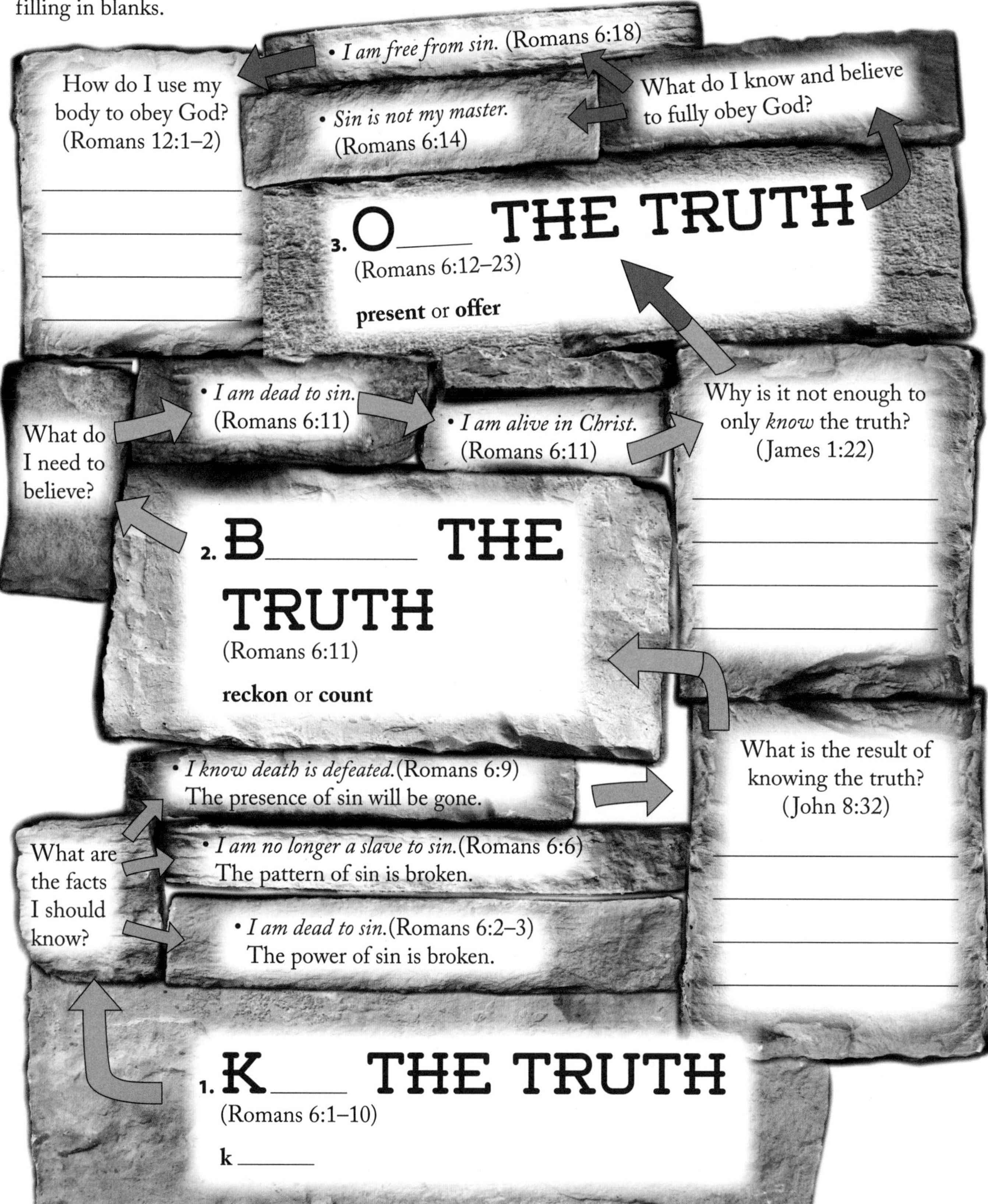

• *I am free from sin.* (Romans 6:18)
How do I use my body to obey God? (Romans 12:1–2)
• *Sin is not my master.* (Romans 6:14)
What do I know and believe to fully obey God?
3. O____ THE TRUTH
(Romans 6:12–23)
present or **offer**
• *I am dead to sin.* (Romans 6:11)
• *I am alive in Christ.* (Romans 6:11)
What do I need to believe?
Why is it not enough to only *know* the truth? (James 1:22)
2. B________ THE TRUTH
(Romans 6:11)
reckon or **count**
• *I know death is defeated.* (Romans 6:9) The presence of sin will be gone.
What is the result of knowing the truth? (John 8:32)
What are the facts I should know?
• *I am no longer a slave to sin.* (Romans 6:6) The pattern of sin is broken.
• *I am dead to sin.* (Romans 6:2–3) The power of sin is broken.
1. K____ THE TRUTH
(Romans 6:1–10)
k ______

Name ______________________________

Romans: Walking in the Spirit

1. Paul described himself as wretched, meaning **miserable or shameful in defeat**. What did his feeling of wretchedness stem from? (Hint: Read Romans 7:21–24.)

____

____

2. What would you do in this situation? You go to buy a refill drink at school. You see that the cafeteria cashier is not looking. You know that if you hurry, she will never see you since she is busy. You could use the refill money for the missions offering that you forgot to bring extra money for. So you put the money in your pocket and hurry on. As you are leaving, you notice some of the younger students who are watching you. Is the decision of what to do a struggle for you? Write and explain your decision.

____

____

____

____

3. Evaluate the scenarios in the middle column. Place an **X** in the appropriate column to show if the scenario describes a person either giving in to sin or yielding to God's righteousness.

Giving In to Sin	Scenarios	Yielding to God's Righteousness
	a. My best friend has the nicest clothes of anybody I know. I will do anything to get clothes like his.	
	b. I will leave this money right where I found it so the person it belongs to can claim it.	
	c. I had planned to lie if I got caught cheating. But now the teacher is asking me about the test, and I know I need to tell the truth.	
	d. I want to visit my friend next door, but I know she does wrong things at her house. I could go to another friend's house, but that will not be as fun. I will go next door, but if my friend starts to do something bad, I will leave.	
	e. I need to repay my older brother for the money he loaned me. My birthday is next week, and I will get gift money. I plan to use that money to buy something for myself.	
	f. I auditioned for a part in the play. When I sang, several of my classmates laughed at me. I felt humiliated. I will never be friends with them again!	

4. Read Romans 8:5. Then explain how you can make the better choice in every situation.

____

12.2 Romans: Walking in the Spirit

1. Samson and Samuel were two men who were used by God (Hebrews 11:32–34) but used in different ways. Read the Scriptures below and explain how these men listened to and obeyed God. Then read Romans 7:22–24 to evaluate whether they were slaves to their sin nature.

Samson	Samuel
• Although Samson had a godly heritage (Judges 13:24–25), he departed from obeying God. How did Samson respond to God at the end of his life? (Judges 16:20 and 16:28) __________ __________ __________	• As a youth, Samuel learned to listen to God and obey Him. (1 Samuel 3:10 and 3:19) How did Samuel describe his obedience to God throughout his life? (1 Samuel 12:2 and 12:23) __________ __________ __________
• Did Samson show a pattern of being a slave to his sin nature? Explain. __________ __________ __________	• Did Samuel show a pattern of being a slave to his sin nature? Explain. __________ __________ __________

2. Are you usually more like Samson or Samuel in the way you listen to and obey God? Rate yourself on the scale below by placing an **X** on the line where you think you belong.

?

-3 -2 -1 0 +1 +2 +3

Samson **Samuel**

3. Both of these men made choices that led to more enslavement to sin or greater sensitivity to God. You do the same. Identify the choices below as producing either slavery or freedom. On the blanks, write an **S** for **slavery** or an **F** for **freedom**.

__ ignore God's truth

__ choose to obey God's Word

__ seek my own desires

__ pray and seek godly advice

__ rely on feelings for decision making

__ listen carefully for God's decision

God can use any person committed to Him, but some people will be used more powerfully because they have learned to listen to and obey God. God can use you too!

Name ______________________________

Romans: Walking in the Spirit 12.3

Romans 8:18–25 declares with hope that all creation anxiously waits to be released from the curse of sin. It waits to be restored back to what God had originally intended.

1. Read the verses. Then describe what will happen in each part of God's creation when it again becomes very good (Genesis 1:31).

a. animal life (Isaiah 11:6–9)	______________________ ______________________
b. the earth (Ezekiel 34:27–29)	______________________ ______________________
c. believers (1 Corinthians 15:49–53)	______________________ ______________________

Scripture explains the Person and role of the Holy Spirit. Match the explanations with their correct reference by placing the correct letter on the lines.

2. The Holy Spirit empowers believers.
a. Acts 1:8 **c.** 2 Corinthians 1:22
b. Romans 8:11

__ comes with power for witnessing

__ put into believers' hearts

__ gives life to mortal bodies

3. The Holy Spirit equips believers.
a. Galatians 5:22–23
b. 1 Corinthians 12:4–11, Romans 12:4–11

__ gives spiritual gifts

__ gives spiritual fruit

4. The Holy Spirit enables believers.
a. Acts 9:31 **c.** John 16:7–8 **e.** Romans 8:16
b. John 14:26 **d.** John 16:13

__ bears witness or testifies that believers are God's children

__ convicts of sin, righteousness, and judgment

__ comforts or encourages

__ helps or counsels, teaches, and reminds

__ guides into all truth

Ships navigate through dangerous waters with the help of buoys. In one rocky harbor, a captain was assured of safe passage by using buoys to help him navigate. Likewise, God helps Christians in life.

5. Read Psalm 119:105, Proverbs 19:20, and John 16:13. List each thing or Person used by God to guide believers to wisdom and victory as they are conformed into the image of Christ.

____

12.4 *Romans: Walking in the Spirit*

Even though suffering because of trials and troubles is hard, it cannot separate a believer from God's love. Some people have wrong beliefs about suffering. Read some wrong beliefs and then use the solution passage to counter the wrong beliefs with a biblical answer. Write the biblical solution on the lines.

Wrong Beliefs About Suffering	Solutions
1. Suffering destroys your faith in God.	Solution (James 1:2–4): ______________________ ______________________
2. Suffering proves that since you are weak, you should just give up.	Solution (2 Corinthians 12:9): ______________________ ______________________
3. Suffering should be understood.	Solution (Isaiah 55:8–9): ______________________ ______________________
4. Suffering shows you have sinned.	Solution (Hebrews 12:2–4): ______________________ ______________________

Every believer can be secure in God's love. Unscramble the letters to create a word that completes the sentences. Then read the sentences to be encouraged about believers' security in God's love.

Regardless of the situation ...

5. Jesus will still save the lost when they __________ to Him.
meoc

6. Jesus will still __________ people.
vleo

7. The ______________________ will still work in people.
olyH tpiiSr

8. God will still give ____________________ to people.
ingsssbel

9. The ____________ will still have all the answers.
lbBie

10. ______________ will still work.
eyrPar

11. God will still ______________ sanctification for His people.
oideprv

Name ______________________________

Thanksgiving 13.1

1. Read the Scriptures. Then create a one-sentence title for each section of the time line.

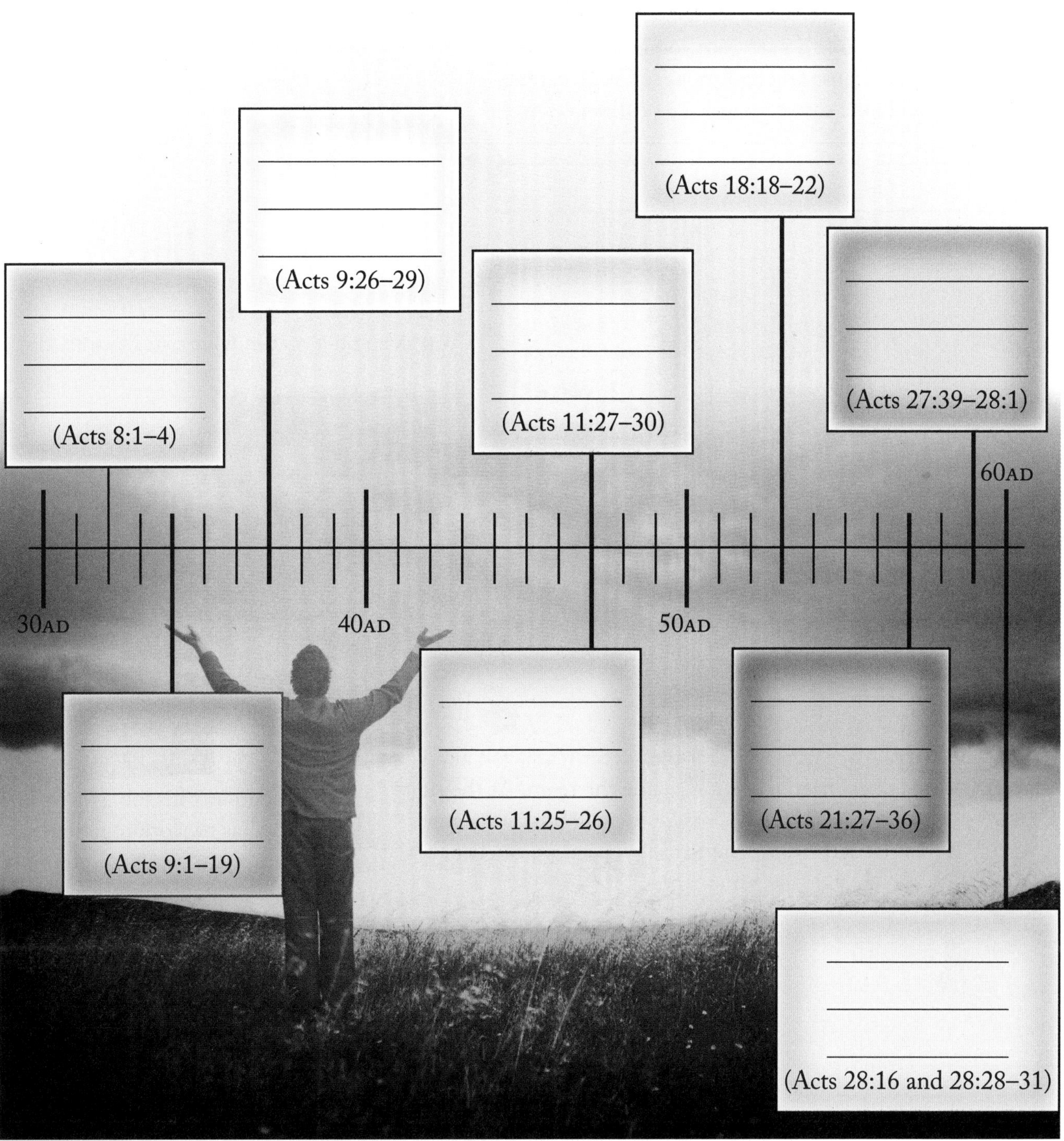

2. Paul had many reasons for thanksgiving. Review the summary of his life from the time line above. Then read Philippians 3:7–11. What reasons did Paul have for his thankfulness?

____

____

____

13.2 Thanksgiving

Read the scenarios that show both positive and negative situations. Tell how you could show an attitude of gratitude to God in each situation.

1. A friend invites you to a party, but you have to decline. You cannot go because you had promised your parents that you would take care of your little brother.

2. Your elderly grandma needs care and comes to live with you. She stays in your room, and you sleep on a mat in your sister's room.

3. You won a prize at a competition and received a cash reward.

4. After trying out for the soccer team, you and your best friend, Manuel, made the team. At the first game, Manuel scored two goals and was named Player of the Game. But you sat on the bench most of the game.

5. Your dad lost his job. Now your family has to work together to come up with ways to save money. His unemployment means you will not get the cool new tennis shoes you wanted.

6. You have been trying to practice a thankful habit, but today everything has gone wrong. A final challenge was a surprise quiz from your teacher. Your friend leans over to you and asks, "What can you be thankful for about this?"

Name ______________________________

Thanksgiving 13.3

Light often describes God's kingdom and the way believers are supposed to conduct themselves. Use the Scriptures to fill in the missing word. Write the letters of each word on the letter blanks. Then look for the secret word in the box and complete the sentence in Exercise 7.

1. Matthew 5:14—You are the light of the ___.

2. Matthew 5:16—Let your light ___ before men.

3. Psalm 36:9—In Your light we see ___.

4. 1 John 1:7—When we walk in the light, we have ___ with other believers.

5. John 3:21—He who walks in ___ comes into the light.

6. John 1:5—The light shines in the ___.

1. _ _ _ [_] _
2. _ _ [_] _ _
3. _ _ [_] _ _
4. _ _ _ _ _ _ _ _ [_] _ _
5. _ _ _ [_] _
6. _ _ _ _ _ _ _ [_] _

7. All believers should be _ _ _ _ _ _ in the world.

Follow the directions.

8. Write two sentences describing how a believer's light should affect others.

____

____

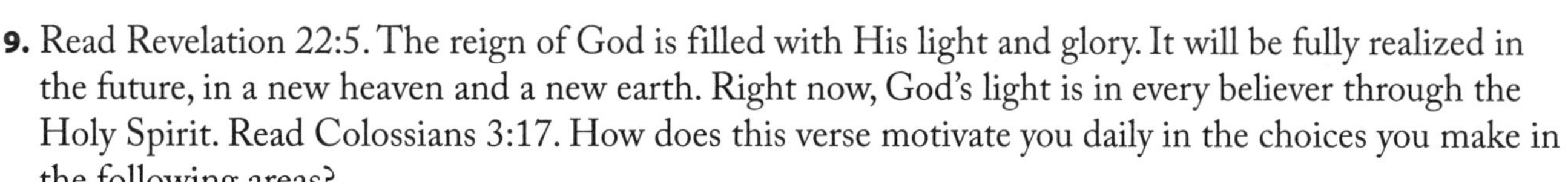

9. Read Revelation 22:5. The reign of God is filled with His light and glory. It will be fully realized in the future, in a new heaven and a new earth. Right now, God's light is in every believer through the Holy Spirit. Read Colossians 3:17. How does this verse motivate you daily in the choices you make in the following areas?

entertainment ______________________________

attitudes ______________________________

friends ______________________________

hobbies ______________________________

13.4 Thanksgiving

Expressing tribute to God helps believers live a life of thankfulness and praise toward Him.

1. Read the following Scriptures: Hebrews 12:15, 2 Timothy 3:1–4, and Colossians 3:8. In the boxes, write a couple of words or phrases describing the consequences of being unthankful.

2. Use the acrostic to list attributes of God that you are thankful for.

P ______________________________

R ______________________________

A ______________________________

I ______________________________

S ______________________________

E ______________________________

Name ____________________

Romans: Conforming to Christ

14.1

1. Believers should not be conformed, or be like the world. Instead, they should be transformed, or changed into Christ as new. They should mature with strong faith and godly habits shown in all they do, say, and think. Draw arrows toward the brain to show phrases that should be added to the thinking of a believer. Draw arrows away from the brain to show which should be rejected. Note the examples.

I can decide what I want to watch without considering that I am transformed in Christ.

I can do whatever I want when I am away from school or home.

I can keep secrets from God.

I will choose godly friends as my best friends.

I will keep a prayer journal.

I can get even with those who hurt me.

I will listen and obey my parents.

I will develop sensitivity to the Holy Spirit.

I will be careful about what I look at.

I can develop a habit of Bible reading.

I will speak out against the evil I see.

I will think about ways I can get close to sinning without sinning.

I will pretend to enjoy Bible class.

I will talk to God every day.

2. Being transformed in Christ is being changed into something new. Christians then become living sacrifices to live fully for Him. Read these three Bible passages that describe a living sacrifice. Then answer the questions briefly.

a. Genesis 22:1–12

- Who was the living sacrifice? ____________________
- Why did he not fight or run away? ____________________
- What did Abraham expect to happen? (Hint: Hebrews 11:19) ____________________

b. Hebrews 9:26–28

- Who was the living sacrifice? ____________________
- How was this His own choice? (John 10:18) ____________________
- What is the believer's benefit? (Romans 8:32) ____________________

c. Romans 12:1–2

- Who are the living sacrifices? ____________________
- Why does God want them to be living sacrifices? ____________________
- Who holds the responsibility for conforming to Christ and having a transformation of mind? ____________________

14.2 Romans: Conforming to Christ

Spiritual gifts listed in Romans 12 are in the left-hand column. Read them and the requests for help on the right. Decide which gift and description on the left would best serve each need on the right. Write the correct letter on the blanks.

___ **1.** Prophesying: declaring truth boldly for God

___ **2.** Serving: sensitively responding to needs and fulfilling them

___ **3.** Teaching: clearly communicating God's truth for practical application

___ **4.** Exhorting: encouraging others toward excellence

___ **5.** Giving: generosity with time, talents, and money

___ **6.** Leading: directing and motivating others to complete goals

___ **7.** Showing mercy: showing genuine empathy through tenderness and care

a. I do not understand this Bible verse. Can you explain it to me clearly and help me apply it?

b. I am so sad. No one knows how badly I hurt. Please help me feel better.

c. If I ask you a question, will you tell me the honest truth? I just want to hear what God says.

d. I know a lady on my block who needs some groceries. Can you buy some to give to her?

e. This project seems too big. Can you help organize willing people and direct them to finish it well?

f. Everyone is exhausted and fumbling. Can you say something to help us keep doing our best?

g. All of these little things need to be done. I will help in any way that I can.

Answer the questions and follow the directions.

8. Review this list. Which gift has the Holy Spirit enabled you or someone you know to do? Explain.

____

____

____

9. Out of a heart of love, believers serve others and glorify God. From Romans 12:9–16, choose six phrases that should describe a believer's life and write them on the arrows below.

10. Where does this heart of love come from? Read 1 John 4:19 and write your answer below.

____

Name ____

Romans: Conforming to Christ 14.3

How you respond to enemies or difficult relationships reveals a lot about your confidence in God. Follow the arrows in the word web to fill in the four **R**s of good relationships. Look up the references. Then fill in the blanks from the Word Bank to complete the explanations. You will not need all the words.

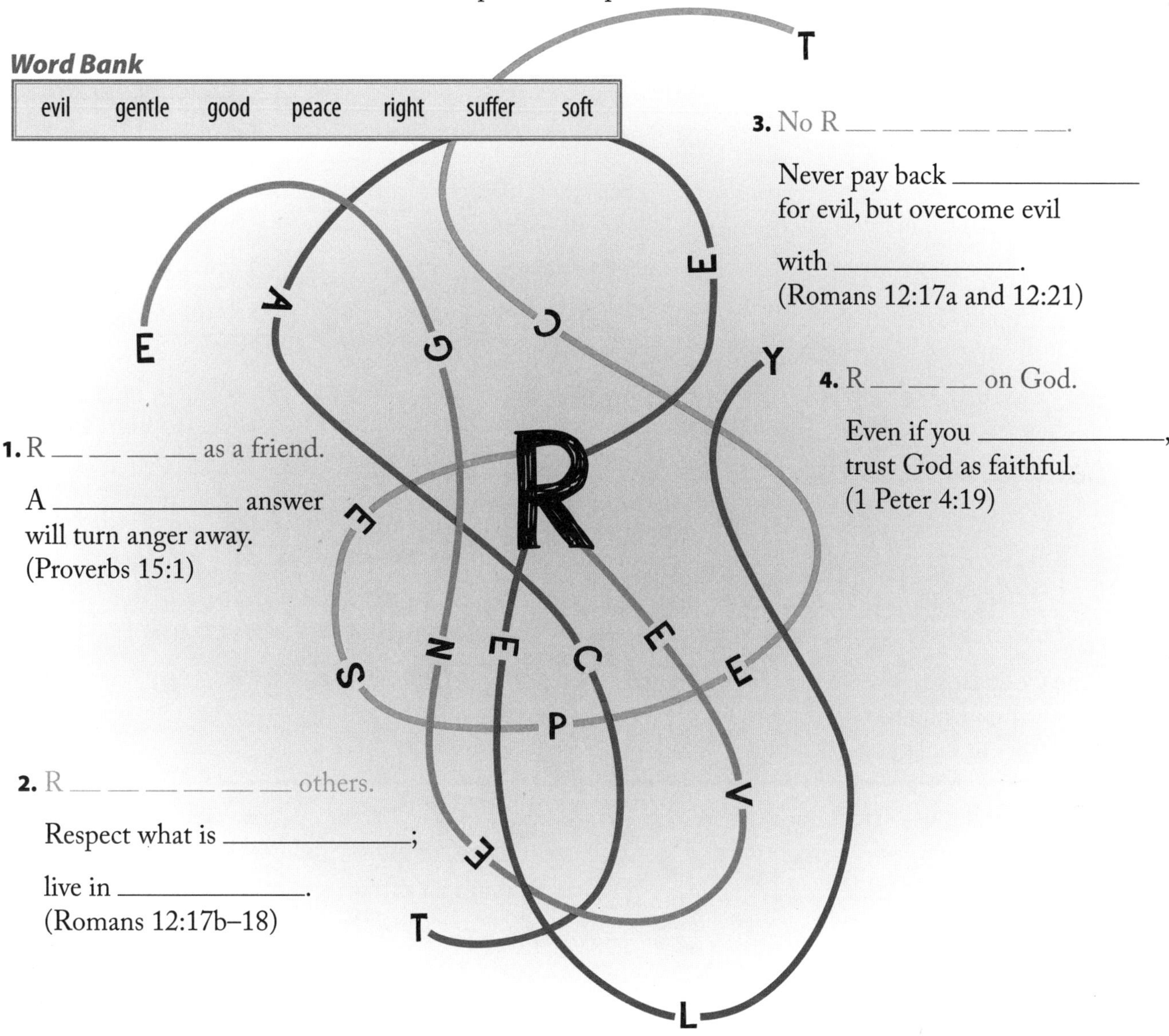

Word Bank

evil	gentle	good	peace	right	suffer	soft

1. R __ __ __ __ as a friend.

A ____________ answer will turn anger away. (Proverbs 15:1)

2. R __ __ __ __ __ __ __ others.

Respect what is ____________;

live in ____________.
(Romans 12:17b–18)

3. No R __ __ __ __ __ __ __.

Never pay back ____________ for evil, but overcome evil

with ____________.
(Romans 12:17a and 12:21)

4. R __ __ __ on God.

Even if you ____________, trust God as faithful.
(1 Peter 4:19)

How would you describe a good friend? Use the acronym **FRIEND** below to write a descriptive word for each letter. Remember the Scriptures you read above.

5. F ________________________

R ________________________

I ________________________

E ________________________

N ________________________

D ________________________

14.4 *Romans: Conforming to Christ*

Denying oneself involves putting your desires aside to follow God's will into maturity. Deep roots produce good fruit and strong, mature Christians. Begin with roots in Exercise 1 and follow the directions to find the sources for the good fruits. Then complete Exercise 2 concerning what those fruits are and Exercise 3.

Code Box					
	6	7	8	9	10
1	U	E	W	J	B
2	H	V	P	M	R
3	Y	G	A	O	F
4	X	D	K	S	I
5	L	T	C	Z	N

___ (3, 10) (3, 8) (4, 10) (5, 7) (2, 6) (3, 10) (1, 6) (5, 6) (5, 10) (1, 7) (4, 9) (4, 9)

(4, 9) (1, 7) (5, 6) (3, 10) - (5, 8) (3, 9) (5, 10) (5, 7) (2, 10) (3, 9) (5, 6)

(3, 7) (1, 7) (5, 10) (5, 7) (5, 6) (1, 7) (5, 10) (1, 7) (4, 9) (4, 9)

(2, 8) (3, 8) (5, 7) (4, 10) (1, 7) (5, 10) (5, 8) (1, 7)

(3, 7) (3, 9) (3, 9) (4, 7) (5, 10) (1, 7) (4, 9) (4, 9)

(5, 6) (3, 9) (2, 7) (1, 7)

(1, 9) (3, 9) (3, 6)

(2, 8) (1, 7) (3, 8) (5, 8) (1, 7)

(4, 8) (4, 10) (5, 10) (4, 7) (5, 10) (1, 7) (4, 9) (4, 9)

2. Use the Code Box to fill in the spiritual fruit above. Check your answers in Galatians 5:22–23.

---

1. Circle the good roots. Cross out the bad roots.

Desire God's Word.

Turn from sin.

Submit to authority.

Make fun of godly things.

Accept God's righteousness.

Love God.

Conform to the world.

Do not forgive.

Glorify God in unity.

Do mean things to others.

Use spiritual gifts to serve others.

Respect others.

Overcome evil with good.

Pray always.

Pay back evil for evil.

Listen to the Holy Spirit.

Cheat the government.

Act nice, but secretly hate.

3. Read Matthew 7:16–18. How can you know if you have good roots or bad roots hidden in your life?

____

____

____

Name ____

1 Corinthians: Correction and Teaching

15.1

The Corinthian Church's sin disappointed Paul. The Church, made up of all believers, is the temple of God today. As each believer shows purity in his or her life, then the whole Church will be able to better demonstrate purity to the world. Briefly answer the questions or follow the directions.

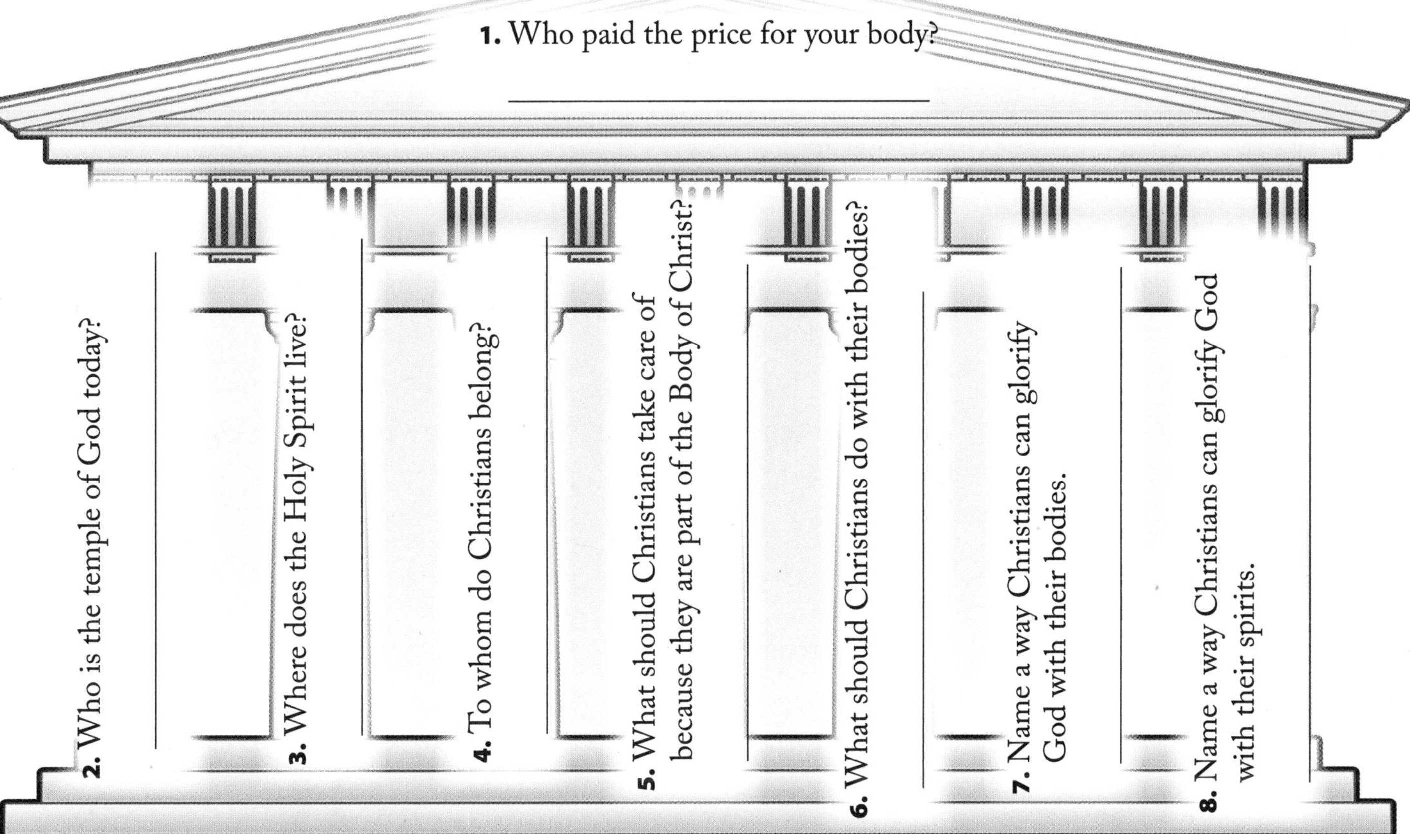

1. Who paid the price for your body?
2. Who is the temple of God today?
3. Where does the Holy Spirit live?
4. To whom do Christians belong?
5. What should Christians take care of because they are part of the Body of Christ?
6. What should Christians do with their bodies?
7. Name a way Christians can glorify God with their bodies.
8. Name a way Christians can glorify God with their spirits.

Look up the Scriptures and circle each reference showing that God dwells in people who believe in Jesus as Savior. Then unscramble the letters next to the answers to complete the missing word in Exercise 15.

9. Romans 8:9 P Romans 5:1 L

10. Ephesians 3:17 T Revelation 1:8 A

11. Luke 2:52 N 1 Corinthians 3:16 R

12. 2 Timothy 1:14 U Galatians 6:2 I

13. John 14:27 S Ephesians 2:22 O

14. 1 John 3:24 R 1 Thessalonians 3:12 G

15. Some believers forget or ignore that God dwells in them. First Corinthians 15:33 warns believers that spending time with evil or bad company c __ __ __ __ __ __ s or spoils good habits or character.

15.2 1 Corinthians: Correction and Teaching

Jesus explained, in Mark 12:30–31, guidelines to help people make good choices for physical and spiritual purity. Purity honors God and shows that the person listens to and follows the Holy Spirit. Fill in the blanks.

1. Love the Lord with all your ____________, ____________, ____________, and ________________.

2. Love your neighbor as ________________.

Circle the choices that follow what Jesus said. Then cross out the choices that do not follow what Jesus said.

3.

study the Bible	keep healthy	speak loving words
watch inappropriate movies	frequently drink a lot of alcohol	visit inappropriate websites
listen to gossip	tell inappropriate jokes	take illegal drugs
sing praise songs	take time to rest and relax	send e-mails that make fun of someone
study for a test	tell others about Jesus	have a party for a neighbor
exercise	help a neighbor do yardwork	

Write more good choices.

4. ________________________, ________________________, ________________________

5. Fill out the certificate and then pray to ask for God's help to fulfill your commitment.

My Commitment

I promise to keep my body and mind pure by ____________________

____

____.

I promise not to ________________________

____.

Name: ________________________

Date: ________________________

Witness: ________________________

Date: ________________________

Name ______________________________

1 Corinthians: Correction and Teaching

15.3

Look up the Scriptures to discover answers to the question, Why does God give spiritual gifts? Write the answer on the white board.

1. 1 Corinthians 12:7

2. 1 Peter 4:10

3. 1 Peter 4:11

4. Ephesians 4:11–12

5. Ephesians 4:13–14

a. ______________________________

b. ______________________________

c. ______________________________

d. ______________________________

e. ______________________________

Think about your class at school. Answer the questions.

6. What kinds of personalities are represented?

____

7. What likes and dislikes are represented?

____

8. What types of abilities are represented?

____

9. How do differences make it easier for your class to work together?

____

10. What might help your class work together better?

____

11. What impact could your class have on your school if everyone lived in unity?

____

____

15.4 *1 Corinthians: Correction and Teaching*

1. Resurrection of Christ

Read 1 Corinthians 15:5–8. Write the proof Paul gave to show that Jesus had risen from the dead. After Jesus' resurrection, the following people saw Him:

____

____

____

____

____

2. Resurrection of the Dead

Read 1 Corinthians 15:22 and fill in the blanks. Paul contrasted people and God: in Adam all ______, but in Christ, all are made ___________.

3. Resurrection of the Physical Body

Fill in the chart on the basis of these specific verses from 1 Corinthians 15.

Verse Number	Believers' Bodies on Earth	Believers' Bodies in the Resurrection
40	terrestrial or earthly	___________
42	corruptible or perishable	___________
44	natural body	___________
54	mortal	___________

4. Resurrection Victory

Refer to 1 Corinthians 15:57 and 15:58. What three qualities do believers have because of victory through the Lord Jesus Christ?

a. ____

b. ____

c. ____

Name ________________________________

1 Corinthians: Love 16.1

God's type of love focuses on other people. Refer to 1 Corinthians 13:4–7. Complete the chart by explaining how the characteristics are seen or not seen in someone who focuses on others versus someone who is self-focused. Some answers have been filled in for you as examples.

Characteristics of Love	Others First	Self First
suffers long or is patient	is very patient, waits for someone without complaining	
is kind		is unkind, uncaring, critical
does not envy		is jealous, wants everything someone else has
does not parade itself or boast, is not puffed up or proud	is humble, wants to compliment others	makes sure everyone notices him or her, boasts about his or her accomplishments
does not act rudely, does not seek its own		is merciless to others, always wants to get his or her own way
is not provoked or easily angered	is easy to get along with, does not get upset when things go wrong	
thinks no evil or keeps no record of wrongs, does not rejoice in iniquity or delight in evil but rejoices in the truth.	always believes the best about a person, is quick to encourage and build others up	
bears all things or always protects, believes all things or always trusts, is always hopeful, endures all things or perseveres		gives up easily, is negative, thinks everything is poorly done, has a bad attitude and is not willing to work things out

16.2 1 Corinthians: Love

Love motivated Jesus to come to the earth and die on a cross for everyone's sin. Followers of Christ can show God's love to others. Look at the pictures carefully. Then answer the questions and fill in the blanks.

1. What is the problem shown?

____

____

Someone motivated by God's love might

____

____

______________________________.

2. What is the problem shown?

____

____

Someone motivated by God's love might

____

____

______________________________.

First Corinthians 16:14 reminds Christians to do everything out of love. Give an example of something motivated by God's love that you could do in the future …

3. at home. ______________________________

____

4. at school. ______________________________

____

5. at church. ______________________________

____

Follow the directions.

6. Write something that you have already said or done that was motivated by love.

____

7. Write something that someone has said to you or done for you that was motivated by love.

____

Name ______________________________

1 Corinthians: Love

16.3

Read the Scriptures. Then match the people to the type of love they are showing.

1. Jesus (John 13:1) •

2. Barnabas and Paul (Acts 15:25) •

3. Dorcas (Acts 9:36) •

4. Paul and Timothy (Colossians 1:1) •

5. Paul and Silas (Acts 15:40) •

6. Stephen (Acts 7:59–60) •

• agape

• phileo

The five love languages are physical touch, words of affirmation, quality time, gifts, and acts of service. Look at the pictures and identify all the ways the person or people are showing love.

16.4 1 Corinthians: Love

First John 4:16–18 contrasts fear and love. Some people obey God out of fear of being punished or making God angry. But God desires His followers to obey Him on the basis of love and a desire to do what pleases Him. When people love God, they choose not to be ruled by fear and choose to love others.

1. Look up the Scriptures and decide what kind of fear could be overcome by an understanding of the Bible truths.

Fear of ...

a. 1 John 1:5 ______________________________

b. John 3:36 ______________________________

c. Philippians 4:19 ______________________________

d. John 15:13–15 ______________________________

e. James 5:14 ______________________________

f. Romans 8:35–37 ______________________________

Love never fails. The more Christians mature in their relationship with God, the more they will think of others first. Also, they will better understand the importance of love.

2. Read the situations below and tell how you could respond in love.

a. You ask your mom if you can go to a party Friday night. She says no because your family is going to celebrate your brother's birthday. How could you respond in a loving way?

____

____

____

b. Your best friend spends the afternoon studying at your house. His idea of studying is to copy all your answers. Think about whether allowing him to copy them is a loving act. If not, how could you respond in love?

____

____

____

c. You and a group of friends walk by another group of friends on the way home from school. One of the girls in that group is being bullied, and she looks scared. You want to say something to defend the girl and want your group of friends to back you up. But, you wonder what your friends will think. How could you show love to the frightened girl?

____

____

____

Name ______________________________

Christmas 17.1

The Young Man and the Squirrels

Read the story and then answer the questions.

A young man was working in the garage when something out of the corner of his eye caught his attention. He looked through the open door to see a squirrel scurrying around the front lawn and burying acorns. After a while, he noticed that there were other squirrels across the street. He watched as they would run and leap from one tree to another, high above the street, in order to cross safely to the other side to bury or retrieve food. He enjoyed watching the furry creatures, and he loved them.

The next day, the city's tree trimmers cut back some of the higher branches. The squirrels could no longer run along the treetops to get from one side of the street to the other. As the squirrels discovered this, they ran down the tree trunks to the curb and tried to cross the street, dodging dangerously between passing cars and trucks. Alarmed, the young man tried to shoo them away from the street. But in fear of the young man, the squirrels simply ran farther down the street to scamper across. Then many more squirrels, unable to find their way across the street from branch to branch safely as before, began running back and forth across the street in deadly pursuit of making it across alive. The young man could do nothing to stop them. He knew it would be only a matter of time before they would be struck and killed by passing traffic. "If only I could become one of them, then they would not be afraid of me," he thought. "If only I could speak their language, run among them, and warn them not to cross in the middle of traffic. Then they would understand me and be saved!"

1. Why were the squirrels in danger? ______________________________

____

2. What did the young man try to do that failed? ______________________________

____

3. What did the young man finally wish that he could do? ______________________________

____

4. How is this story reflective of what Jesus Christ did for all people? ______________________________

____

____

5. What is the difference between what the young man could not do and what Jesus Christ did?

____

____

17.2 Christmas

Christmas joy is expressed throughout the Christmas account and by today's believers. Use the Word Bank to fill in the blanks next to the clues. You will not use all the words. Then follow the directions below.

1. Angels declared to the shepherds ___ ___ ___ | ___ | ___ ___ ___ ___ ___ ___ ___ ___ ___ ___.
2. Many people seek a temporary holiday | ___ | ___ ___ ___ ___ ___ ___ ___ ___ ___ ___ ___ ___ ___.
3. Jesus was born to be the ___ ___ ___ ___ ___ | ___.
4. This name means **God with us.** | ___ | ___ ___ ___ ___ ___ ___ ___ ___
5. Special Christmas songs are ___ ___ ___ ___ ___ | ___.
6. The Bible presents God's ___ ___ ___ | ___ | ___.
7. Celebration occurs with the whole ___ ___ | ___ | ___ ___ ___.
8. Jesus came to bring ___ ___ ___ ___ | ___ | ___ ___ ___ ___.
9. They still seek to worship Jesus. ___ ___ | ___ | ___ ___ ___ ___
10. The coming Messiah would be named | ___ | ___ ___ ___ ___.
11. Through Him all sins would be ___ | ___ | ___ ___ ___ ___ ___ ___.
12. Many buy these to give to children. ___ ___ | ___ | ___

Word Bank

- baby boy
- carols
- family
- forgiven
- happiness
- holy night
- Immanuel
- Jesus
- peace on Earth
- salvation
- Savior
- shepherds
- toys
- truth
- wise men

13. Contrast the main focus, activities, and attitudes Christians and non-Christians sometimes show during Christmas. List contrasts on each side under the appropriate heading. List similarities in the middle.

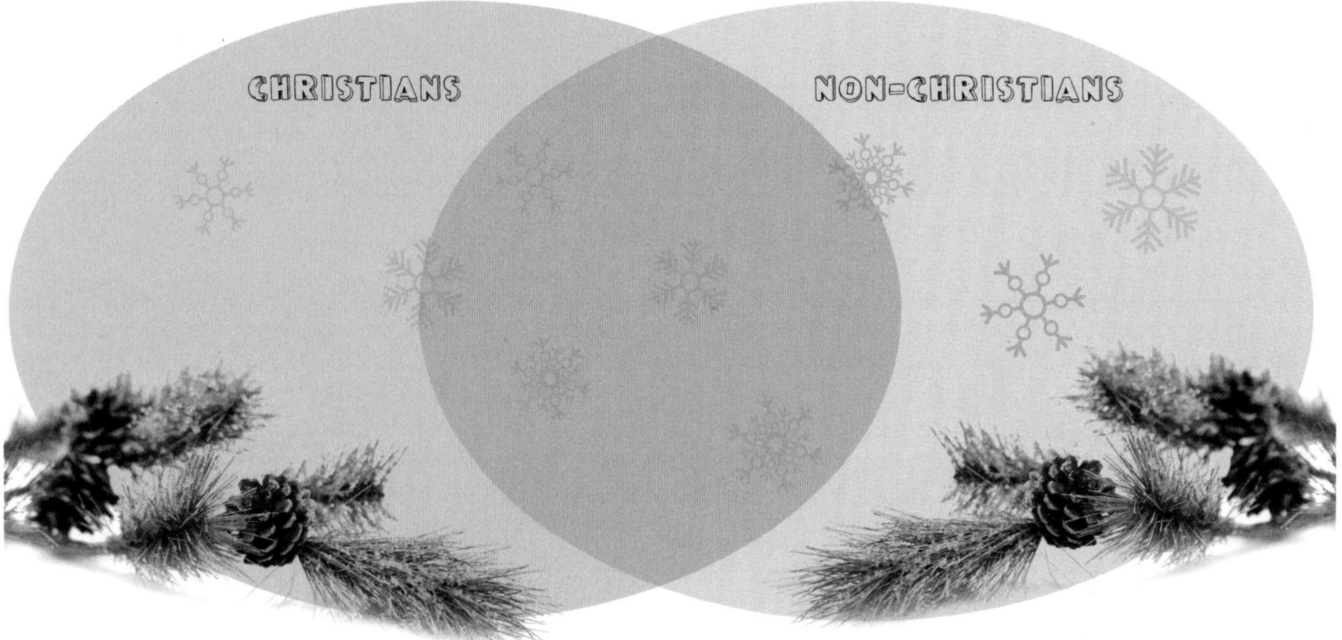

14. Use the Venn diagram to determine which attitudes or activities distract you the most from celebrating the real meaning of Christmas. Take time to pray about having the right focus and godly attitudes about Christmas this year. Ask the Lord to give you His true, lasting joy—not just during the Christmas season but all the time!

Name ______________________________

Christmas 17.3

1. Hope helps you expect a promise to come true, if the promise is from a reliable source. The Bible gives promises that communicate hope because they are true and are from God. The promises of God can be like unwrapping a gift from Him that produces hope. Read the Scripture passages. Then write the correct Scripture reference under the corresponding statements of hope.
SCRIPTURE PROMISES: Romans 5:5, Romans 15:13, 1 Timothy 4:10, Hebrews 6:19, and Hebrews 10:23

Hope does not disappoint; God's love is poured out through the Holy Spirit.

____

Hope is like an anchor to keep believers sure and steadfast.

____

Believers have their hope fixed on the living God, their Savior.

____

The God of hope fills believers with joy and peace by the power of the Holy Spirit.

____

Believers can hold fast to their hope in the promises of God because He is faithful.

____

2. Use the first number in the ordered pair to move to the correct horizontal location on the grid. Then use the second number in the ordered pair to move to the correct vertical location. Write the corresponding letter on the line and continue solving the message from Psalms. The message tells God's response to those who hope in Him.

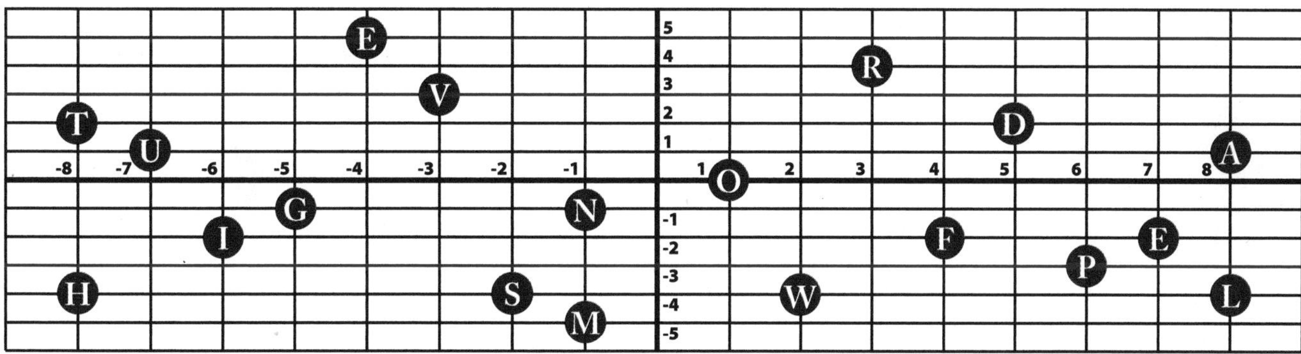

___ ___ ___   ___ ___ ___ ___   ___ ___ ___ ___ ___ ___ ___ ___   ___ ___
(-8, 2) (-8,-4) (-4, 5)   (8,-4) (1, 0) (3, 4) (5, 2)   (5, 2) (-4, 5) (8,-4) (-6,-2) (-5,-1) (-8,-4) (-8, 2) (-2,-4)   (-6,-2) (-1,-1)

___ ___ ___ ___ ___   ___ ___ ___   ___ ___ ___ ___   ___ ___ ___,   ___ ___ ___
(-8, 2) (-8,-4) (1, 0) (-2,-4) (-4, 5)   (2,-4) (-8,-4) (1, 0)   (4,-2) (-4, 5) (8, 1) (3, 4)   (-8,-4) (-6,-2) (-1,-5),   (2,-4) (-8,-4) (1, 0)

___ ___ ___   ___ ___ ___ ___ ___   ___ ___ ___ ___   ___ ___   ___ ___ ___
(6,-3) (-7, 1) (-8, 2)   (-8, 2) (-8,-4) (-4, 5) (-6,-2) (3, 4)   (-8,-4) (1, 0) (6,-3) (-4, 5)   (-6,-2) (-1,-1)   (-8,-4) (-6,-2) (-2,-4)

___ ___ ___ ___ ___ ___ ___ ___ ___   ___ ___ ___ ___.
(-7, 1) (-1,-1) (4,-2) (8, 1) (-6,-2) (8,-4) (-6,-2) (-1,-1) (-5,-1)   (8,-4) (1, 0) (-3, 3) (-4, 5).

___ ___ ___ ___ ___ 147:11 (NIV 2011)
(6,-3) (-2,-4) (8, 1) (8,-4) (-1,-5)

17.4 Christmas

Part of the Christmas account involves three situations in which God presented His peace to fear-filled people. Match the people to three applicable descriptive statements by placing correct letters in the boxes. If needed, use the Bible verses to check your answers.

☐	☐	☐	**1.** Zechariah (Luke 1:11–20)
☐	☐	☐	**2.** Mary
☐	☐	☐	**3.** Shepherds

a. You will have a son—name him John.
b. You will find a baby in a manger.
c. Nothing is impossible with God!
d. Your prayers have been answered.
e. I bring you good news of great joy: a Savior is born!
f. You have found favor with God.
g. You, a virgin, will bear a child, the Messiah.
h. Because of your unbelief, you will be unable to speak.
i. Let us go and see, and then we will tell of this child.

The Christmas account promises peace. Help the students below with their fears by giving advice on the basis of the verses listed. Emphasize the promises God gives for faith to become stronger. Remember that 1 John 4:18 says there is no fear in love.

My grandpa is sick right now. What if he gets worse and dies? Even though he is a Christian, I do not know how I would handle his death.

4. ______________________________

____

____

____

______________ Psalm 23:4 and 116:15

Sometimes I am afraid at home alone. I do not feel safe or protected. My parents are not always there. Honestly, it is scary!

5. ______________________

____

____

____

____

____

____

Proverbs 18:24 and 17:17

I do not have any real friends at school. Does anyone like me? Others make fun of me or pick on me sometimes. I am lonely!

6. ______________________________________

____

____

Psalm 56:3–4

Name ______________________________

2 Corinthians: Truth and Giving

18.1

1. Change occurs because of a truth. God had sent the apostle Paul to share the gospel and strengthen the Corinthian Church. The new believers gained a new faith foundation for their life. Read the parable Jesus told about foundations from Matthew 7:24–27. Draw a line through the weak, wrong foundations and put a check mark in each box next to the solid, right foundations.

- ☐ The Father, Son, and Holy Spirit are all God.
- ☐ I should feel conceited.
- ☐ The Bible is the Word of God.
- ☐ God's grace through faith can save anyone.
- ☐ The wages of sin is eternal death.
- ☐ Everyone will spend eternity either in heaven or hell.
- ☐ Admit, believe, and confess for salvation.
- ☐ God's gift brings eternal life to all who believe.
- ☐ God's grace means I can sin all I want.
- ☐ Truth is whatever someone wants to believe.
- ☐ Jesus rose from the dead.
- ☐ Everyone goes to heaven.
- ☐ If I am good enough, I can go to heaven.
- ☐ All have sinned.
- ☐ Jesus Christ is Lord.
- ☐ Since God loves everyone, all will be saved.

2. Reconciliation is the act of being brought back into relationship. It produces change. Paul did see this change in new believers in Corinth. But he wanted the new believers to be sure to fully obey God's gospel truth to live differently than the people in the sinful city of Corinth. Read 2 Corinthians 5:17–19. Use the acronym **CHANGE** to write phrases describing the change in a Christian's life. One example is given for you.

C orinthians believe	**C** ______________________
H ave a ministry of reconciliation	**H** ______________________
A way with the old things	**A** ______________________
N ew creation	**N** ______________________
G od reconciled me	**G** ______________________
E verything is new	**E** ______________________

18.2 2 Corinthians: Truth and Giving

1. Paul was motivated to share the life-changing truth of the gospel. Use the references and words from the Outline Banks to complete the outline.

I. Characteristics of True Ministers of God

A. ________________ 2 Corinthians 2:7–8

B. ________________ 2 Corinthians 2:14–15

C. ________________ 2 Corinthians 3:17–18

D. ________________ 2 Corinthians 4:6

E. ________________ 2 Corinthians 4:15

Outline Bank
liberty, or freedom forgiveness, comfort, and love to others grace with thanks shining of Christ's light fragrance or aroma of Christ

II. Paul's Motivation

A. ________________ 2 Corinthians 4:16–18

B. ________________ 2 Corinthians 5:14–15

C. ________________ 2 Corinthians 5:17–21

D. ________________ 2 Corinthians 6:1–3

Outline Bank
reconciliation for righteousness eternal, not temporary, nature of life grace without offense love of Christ

2. How is a minister of God like a pot of clay?

____

____

____

Name ______________________________

2 Corinthians: Truth and Giving

18.3

Respond to the scenarios by writing what you would do.

1. You go to church and the pastor is talking about missionaries in Nigeria who need help financially. You have money that you have been saving up for a new skateboard.

____

____

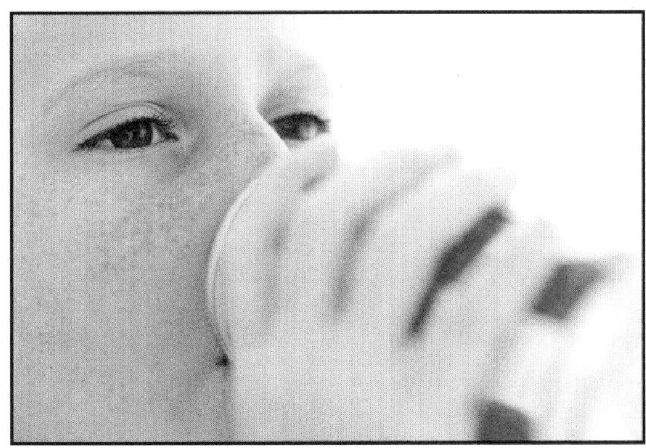

2. Your friend is begging you to give him money to buy a soda out of the soda machine at school. You just received some money for mowing your grandpa's yard and have it in your pocket.

____

____

____

3. Your school is doing a fund-raiser for a charity. The winning class gets a party. All your friends seem to be giving a large sum of money. You do not have a lot of money, but you may be able to borrow from your savings.

____

____

____

4. Your parents give you an allowance every week for doing extra chores around the house. They told you that, this month, you could spend it on whatever you wish.

____

____

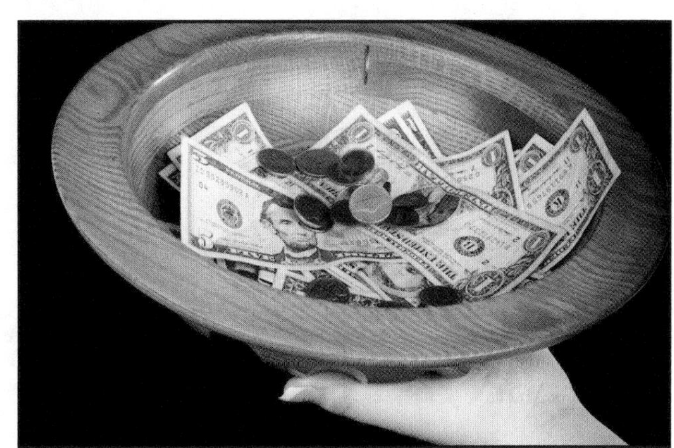

5. You go to the church of a friend for the first time after spending the night at his or her house. The offering plate is passed. You have some change from your spending money in your pocket.

____

____

____

18.4 2 Corinthians: Truth and Giving

1. Read the verses. Then make a check mark in the correct box to show whether the sentences represent a truth or a lie. If the statements are false, explain why on the lines.

   a. Satan's deceptions are always clearly seen. He always shows himself as wicked. (2 Corinthians 11:14)

   ☐ Truth ☐ Lie

   ____

   ____

   ____

   b. Believers should brag about their strengths so that they can become more powerful. (2 Corinthians 12:9)

   ☐ Truth ☐ Lie

   ____

   ____

   ____

   c. Believers should work through weakness, insults, hardships, persecution, and difficulties because they are strong enough to overcome these on their own. (2 Corinthians 12:10)

   ☐ Truth ☐ Lie

   ____

   ____

   ____

2. Use the statements to examine yourself. Make a check mark in the box next to applicable statements.

   ☐ I see God working in mighty ways in my life.

   ☐ God is my ultimate authority.

   ☐ I am known for stirring up trouble and strife.

   ☐ Handling things on my own seems to be working fine.

   ☐ Because of God's love, I think of others more than myself.

   ☐ Gossiping is something I find myself doing often.

Name ______________________________

Galatians: Faith and Fruit

19.1

Read Galatians 4:4–7. Then use the Word Bank to fill in the chart contrasting the bondage of trying to fully obey the Law to earn salvation with freedom in Christ for salvation. Then answer the questions in Exercise 4.

Bondage	Freedom
1. life as a ______________	**1.** life as a ______________
2. life under the ______________	**2.** life in ______________
3. ______________ to receive from God	**3.** being an ______________ of God

Word Bank

Christ
Law
working
son
slave
heir

4. Would you rather be a slave or a son? Why? ______________________________

____

Read the Scriptures. Write what you learn from the verses about the topics noted.

5. Galatians 5:1

a. freedom ______________________________

b. bondage ______________________________

6. Galatians 5:13

a. wrong use of freedom ______________________________

b. right use of freedom ______________________________

7. Galatians 5:14

a. entire law fulfilled or summed up ______________________________

b. loving your neighbor ______________________________

19.2 Galatians: Faith and Fruit

The Bible mentions individual fruits of the Spirit in several places. It also mentions other kinds of fruit in several places. Look up the verses to discover the fruits, note the fruit shapes below, and draw the correct fruit shapes on the lines.

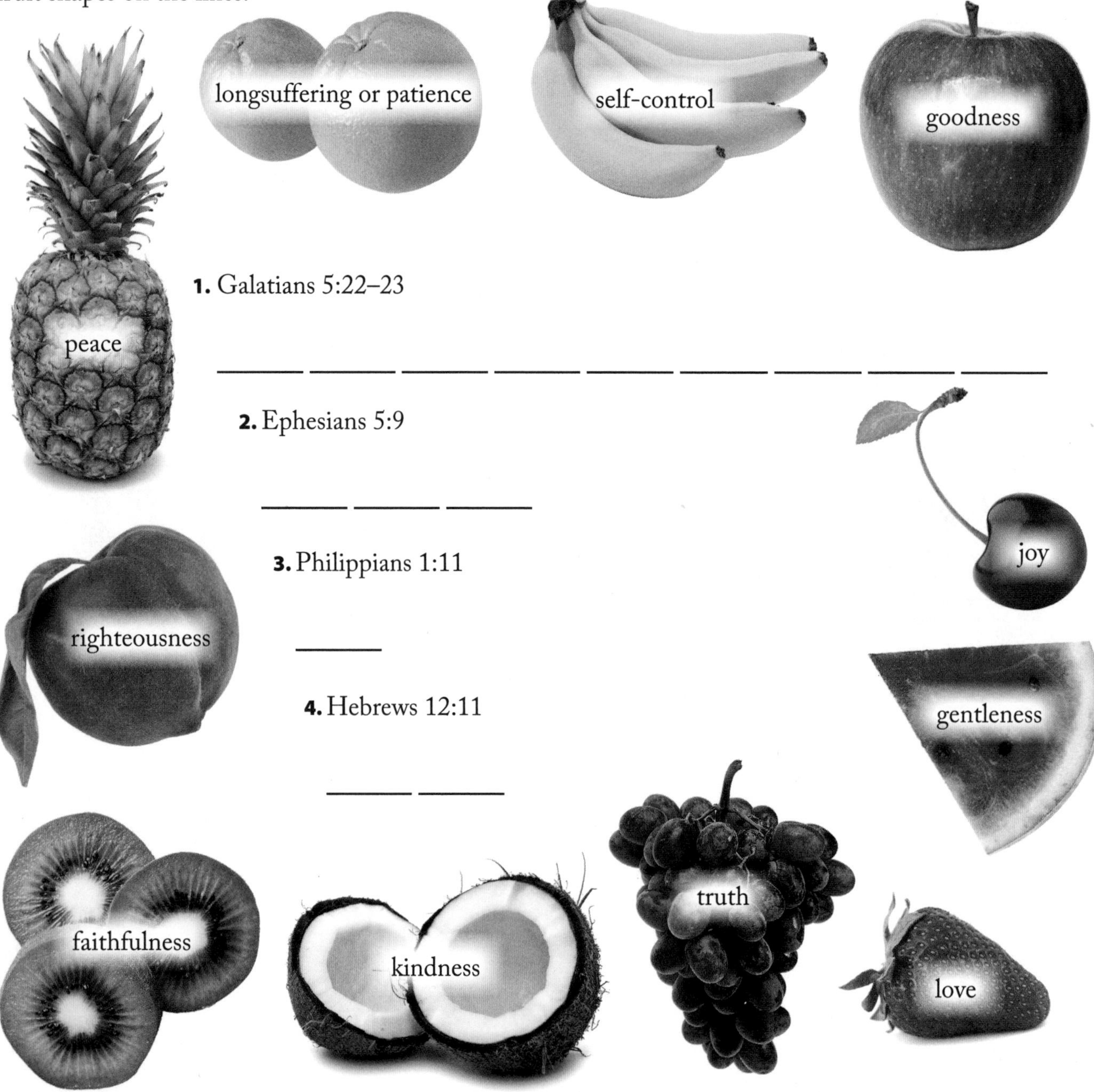

1. Galatians 5:22–23

______ ______ ______ ______ ______ ______ ______ ______ ______

2. Ephesians 5:9

______ ______ ______

3. Philippians 1:11

______

4. Hebrews 12:11

______ ______

Give a practical example of how four fruits of the Spirit could be shown in your classroom. (See your answers to Exercise 1 above.) Place the fruit's name on the first answer line and place your example on the longer line.

5. ____________________ : ____________________________________

6. ____________________ : ____________________________________

7. ____________________ : ____________________________________

8. ____________________ : ____________________________________

Name

Galatians: Faith and Fruit 19.3

For the following scenarios, on the left side, write what fleshly desires you might be tempted to follow. On the right side, write what the Holy Spirit would want you to do. Underneath the pictures, write what fruit from the list in Galatians 5:22–23 could be revealed in these scenarios if you walk in the Spirit.

SINFUL DESIRES

SPIRIT'S DESIRES

1. A girl at school is gossiping about you.

2. A friend shows you something on the computer that you are sure your parents would not want you to see.

3. You did not read the chapter you were supposed to have read for homework.

Follow the directions.

4. Read Galatians 5:24–25. Then write on the lines two ways that the fruit of the Spirit can be produced in a believer's life.

a.

b.

19.4 Galatians: Faith and Fruit

People are always sowing seeds during their life. They will eventually reap the harvest from those seeds. Write the name of the crop that may be harvested on the row connected to the seed packets.

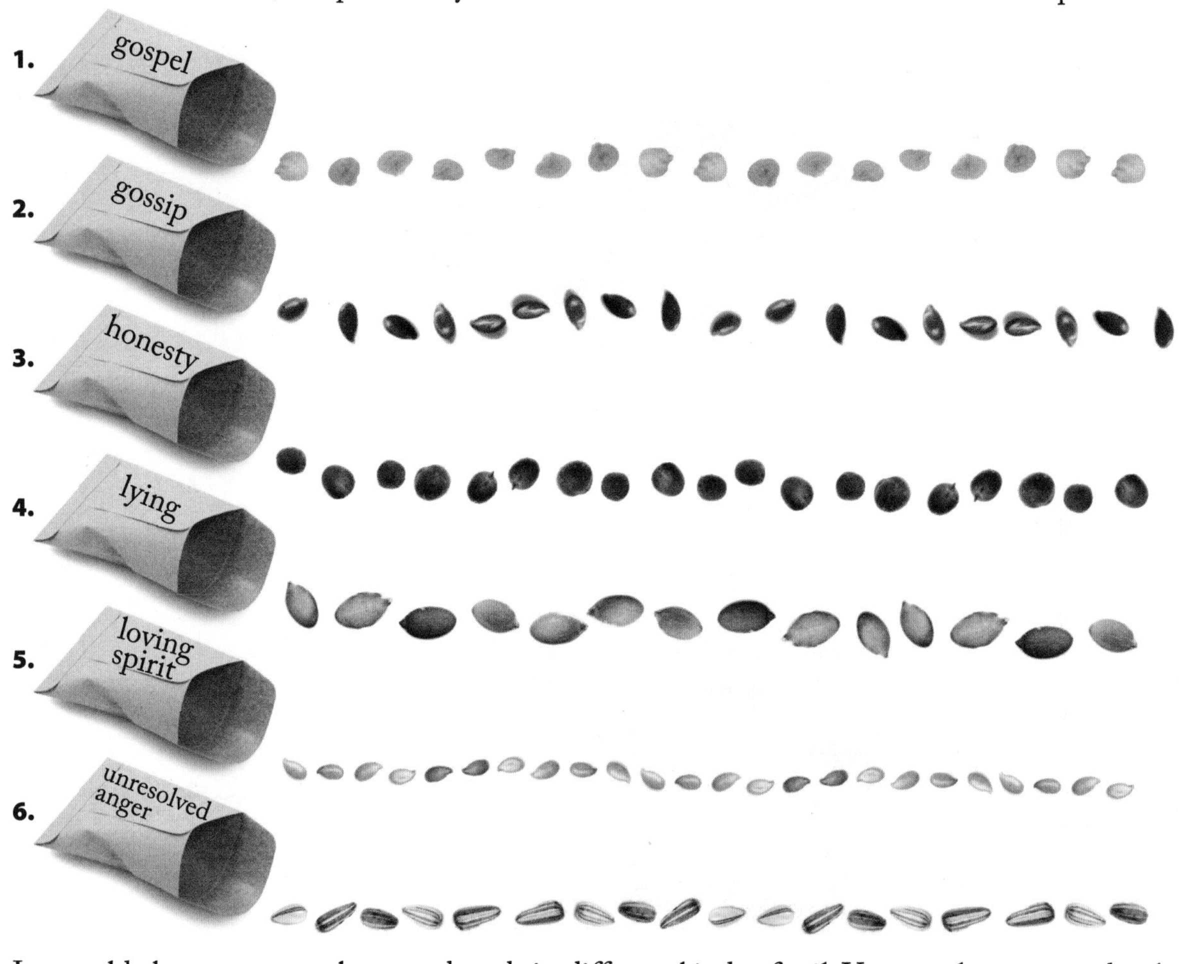

Jesus told about a sower who sowed seeds in different kinds of soil. You are also supposed to be a sower—a sower of God's Word! Read the Scriptures, fill in the blanks, and check the correct boxes that show whether the seed grew and produced.

THE SEED ...

7. Mark 4:2–4

type of soil ______________________ grew ☐ did not grow ☐ produced ☐

8. Mark 4:5–6

type of soil ______________________ grew ☐ did not grow ☐ produced ☐

9. Mark 4:7

type of soil ______________________ grew ☐ did not grow ☐ produced ☐

10. Mark 4:8

type of soil ______________________ grew ☐ did not grow ☐ produced ☐

Read Mark 4:14 and answer the question.

11. What is the seed that is sown? ____

Name ____________________

Ephesians: Unity and Relationships

20.1

1. God revealed the mystery of Christ to Paul. Use the coded letters to fill in the blanks and uncover this mystery. Check your answer in Colossians 1:27.

_ _ _ _ _ _ in you, the _ _ _ _ of _ _ _ _ _

2. A mystery is like a puzzle. Solve the clues below and write the answers in the crossword puzzle. Check your answers using the references.

a. It is not up to you
to try to win the race.
Forgiveness of sins is fully due
to God's amazing ___ (1→).
(Ephesians 1:7)

b. It is not what you do
or whether you are great.
You are made brand-new
by grace and through ___ (2↓).
(Ephesians 2:8)

c. It is not by your ___ (3↓)
or how much you could lift.
It is not because of perks,
for it is God's free ___ (4→).
(Ephesians 2:8–9)

d. Though God did choose
to offer for a while
salvation to the Jews,
now it includes every ___ (5↓).
(Ephesians 3:1 and 3:8)

e. The heirs are all one:
both Jews and Gentiles involved.
Through Christ, God's Son,
the ___ (6→) of Christ at last is solved.
(Ephesians 3:4–6)

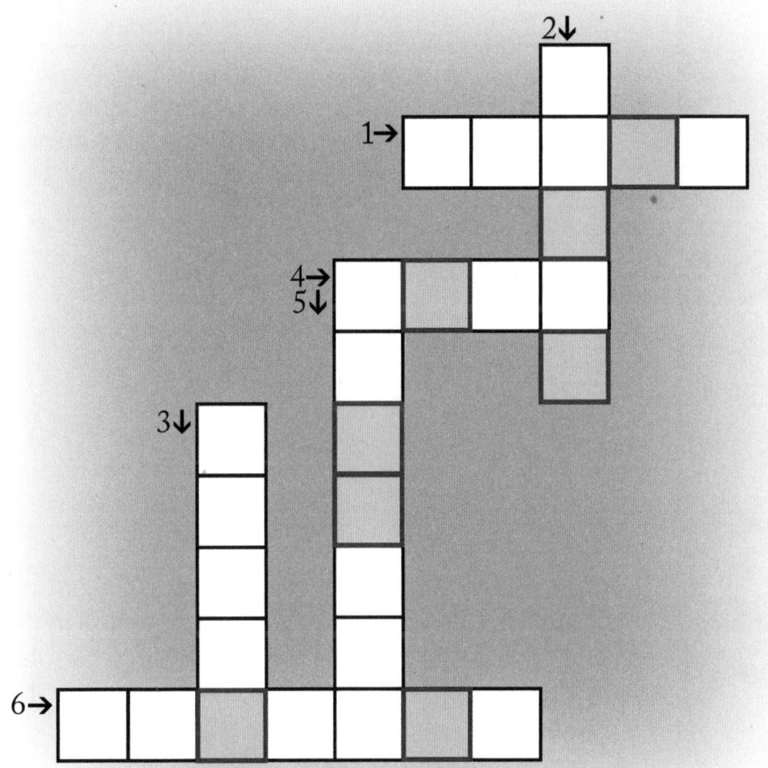

3. Unscramble the letters in the red boxes above to solve the mystery phrase and finish the sentence. This short phrase is used nearly 40 times in Ephesians to describe a believer's new relationship.

- Believers are blessed with every spiritual blessing _ _ _ _ _ _ _ _. (Ephesians 1:3)

20.2 Ephesians: Unity and Relationships

Imagine that Mr. Johnston has to go on vacation. He wants to make sure his students who are having problems get help. So, he has asked you to answer their questions on his blog until he returns. Read the questions below and write your godly answer under each question.

1. I am new to school this year. I made friends quickly but found that some of my friends often get into trouble. They keep asking me to join in. I do not want to get a bad reputation, but I am afraid I will not have any friends if I give up on this group. What should I do?
   Signed, Ryan

   ____

   ____

   ____

   ____

2. My friend Sara talks to me all the time. She even talks to me in class sometimes, and I get into trouble for not paying attention even though I am trying. She seems to need a lot of attention. Sara told me once that she does not have any other friends and that she is lonely. How can I help Sara understand how I feel?
   Signed, Evelyn

   ____

   ____

   ____

   ____

3. My little brother, Ian, got me into trouble. Last weekend, I was walking through the living room with my soccer ball in my hands. Ian took it from me and kicked it, and it broke my mom's candleholder above the fireplace. My mom's rule is no balls in the house, so I got in trouble even though I was only carrying it. I am very angry with my brother and want to get back at him. What should I do?
   Signed, Elijah

   ____

   ____

   ____

   ____

Name ________________________________

Ephesians: Unity and Relationships

1. Listed on the left are tactics Satan may use to attack believers. Draw a line from the attack methods to the piece of armor that would best counter them.

You wonder if you are even saved. •	• belt of truth
You believe lies that deceive or confuse your thinking. •	• breastplate of righteousness
You are kept from the Word and Bible memorization. •	• readiness of the gospel of peace
You delay witnessing to someone. •	• shield of faith
You doubt and do not trust God as much. •	• helmet of salvation
You are tempted with evil ideas and ungodly activities. •	• sword of the Spirit

2. Use the information above to complete the following.

a. Circle the one piece of armor that is used as a weapon of attack.

b. How can believers use it as a weapon to defeat Satan?

____

____

____

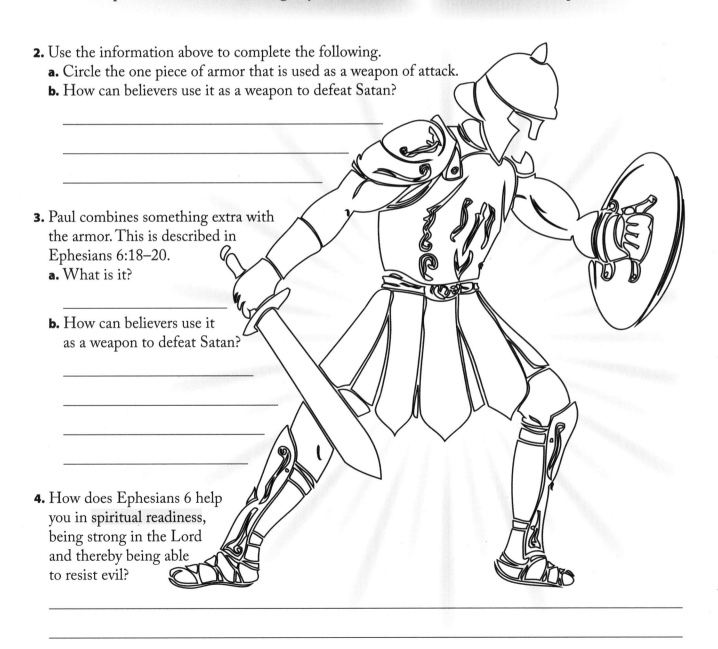

3. Paul combines something extra with the armor. This is described in Ephesians 6:18–20.

a. What is it?

____

b. How can believers use it as a weapon to defeat Satan?

____

____

____

____

4. How does Ephesians 6 help you in spiritual readiness, being strong in the Lord and thereby being able to resist evil?

____

____

20.4 Ephesians: Unity and Relationships

1. In Ephesians 5:1–20, Paul contrasted walking in light and walking in darkness. Look at the Word Bank. Then write the words and phrases that belong with the light and those that belong with darkness in the correct box.

LIGHT

Word Bank

- love
- greed
- sacrifice
- impurities
- foolish talk
- being drunk
- thanksgiving
- being filled with the Spirit
- goodness
- coarse jokes
- righteousness
- truth

2. Read Luke 2:41–52. What was Jesus like at 12? What should you be like as an imitator of Christ? Write your answers on the lines under the correct heading.

Christ's Example to Me	My Response

Name ______________________________

Philippians: Contentment 21.1

1. Ahab thought Naboth's vineyard would make him happy. Paul counted it a joy to suffer for Christ. The thoughts of a person guide his or her actions—whether the person is a king or a prisoner, like Paul was at times. Read the Scriptures and answer the questions about King Ahab and Paul.

	King Ahab's Thoughts	Paul's Thoughts
a. What thoughts did he focus on?	1 Kings 21:2	Acts 16:25
b. Were his thoughts negative or positive?		
c. What was the result?	1 Kings 21:11–16	Acts 16:34
d. Who was responsible for these results?		

2. Give examples of what you look for to either make you happy or give you lasting joy.

____

____

3. Draw lines to match the Scripture references with the question they answer. Then supply the answer to each question.

a. Psalm 16:11 • • Whose joy is in believers? ______________

b. Isaiah 29:19 • • Where do believers find joy? ______________

c. John 15:10–11 • • What is joy based on? ______________

d. 1 Peter 1:8 • • Who rejoices in the Lord? ______________

21.2 Philippians: Contentment

Use the Code Box to identify qualities someone who has the mind of Christ should show and those he or she should not show. Place the correct letter on the blanks to find these qualities.

Code Box
A B C D E F H I L M N O R S T U V Y

The mind of Christ includes ...

1. ___ ___ ___ ___
2. ___ ___ ___ ___ ___ ___ ___ ___ ___
3. ___ ___ ___ ___ ___ ___ ___ ___ ___
4. ___ ___ ___ ___ ___ ___ ___

The mind of Christ does not include ...

5. ___ ___ ___ ___ ___ ___ ___ ___ ___ ___ ___
6. ___ ___ ___ ___   ___ ___ ___ ___ ___ ___ ___ ___
7. ___ ___ ___ ___ ___ ___ ___

Answer the question and follow the directions.

8. What can help a believer have the mind of Christ?

____

____

9. Draw an item that has at least four important parts that make it operate or function. Label these characteristics of unity on four of the parts: **having one mind, being united by love, showing humility**, and **looking out for others' interests**.

10. Explain what would happen to the item you drew if one or more of the parts were missing.

____

____

11. Christian unity can be destroyed when even one of these characteristics is missing. Choose one and give an example of what could happen to Christian relationships without it.

____

____

Name ________________________________

Philippians: Contentment 21.3

Paul reminded Christians that they do not impress God by what they do for Him. Christ's suffering on the cross and resurrection completed everything needed for salvation. As Christians serve others because they have the mind of Christ, they serve out of love and thankfulness for what Jesus has done for them! Read the scenarios and respond to the questions.

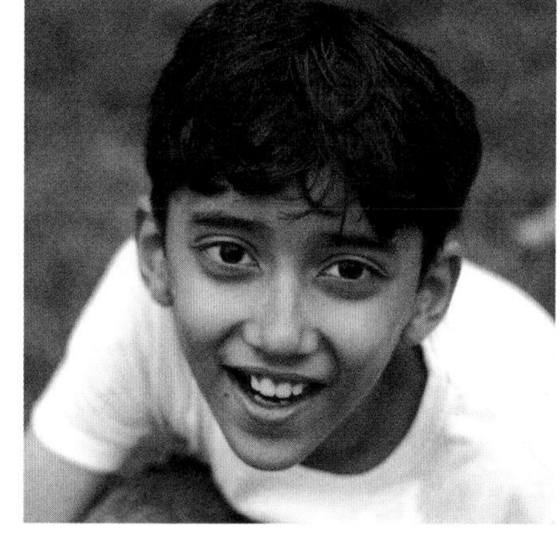

1. Ravi knows his church has a work day scheduled on Saturday to clean a home for some returning missionaries. He wants to impress his youth group leaders who will be there. How would Ravi respond if he remembered Christ's righteousness?

____

____

____

____

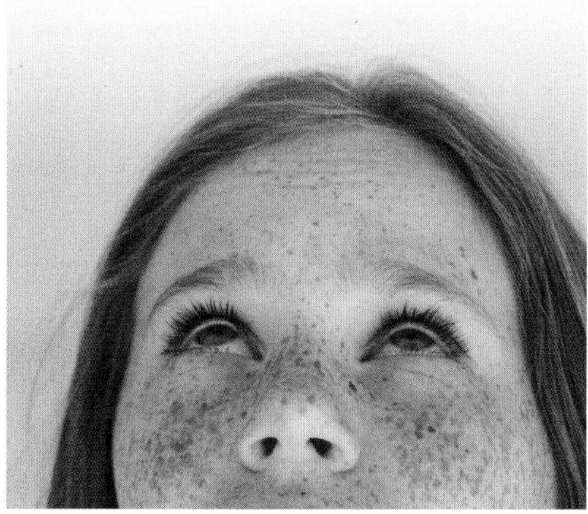

2. Becca hears her friends say that God wants Christians to pray continually. She still feels bad about disobeying her parents last week. She wonders if she would feel better by praying for five minutes several times a day. How would Becca respond if she remembered Christ's righteousness?

____

____

____

Read 1 Timothy 4:12. Paul wanted to be a good example of following Jesus. Timothy's younger age might have caused some people not to listen to Timothy or follow his example. But Paul trusted Timothy to set a good example. Be encouraged by Paul to be a young but good example for Christ! Follow the directions and answer the question.

3. Circle the ways Paul encouraged young people to be good examples.

sports good attitude understanding technology staying healthy good looks purity faith love safety awareness good grades word, or speech conduct or life spirit

4. How are you an example to others of following Christ?

____

____

5. Paul counted his Jewish background as a loss for Christ because his values changed. Give an example of something a believer today may count as a loss even though the world values it.

____

____

21.4 *Philippians: Contentment*

1. Read Philippians 4:8–9 to find God's prescription for right thinking. Find in these verses at least six kinds of thoughts that you can practice. Then write them on the bottles.

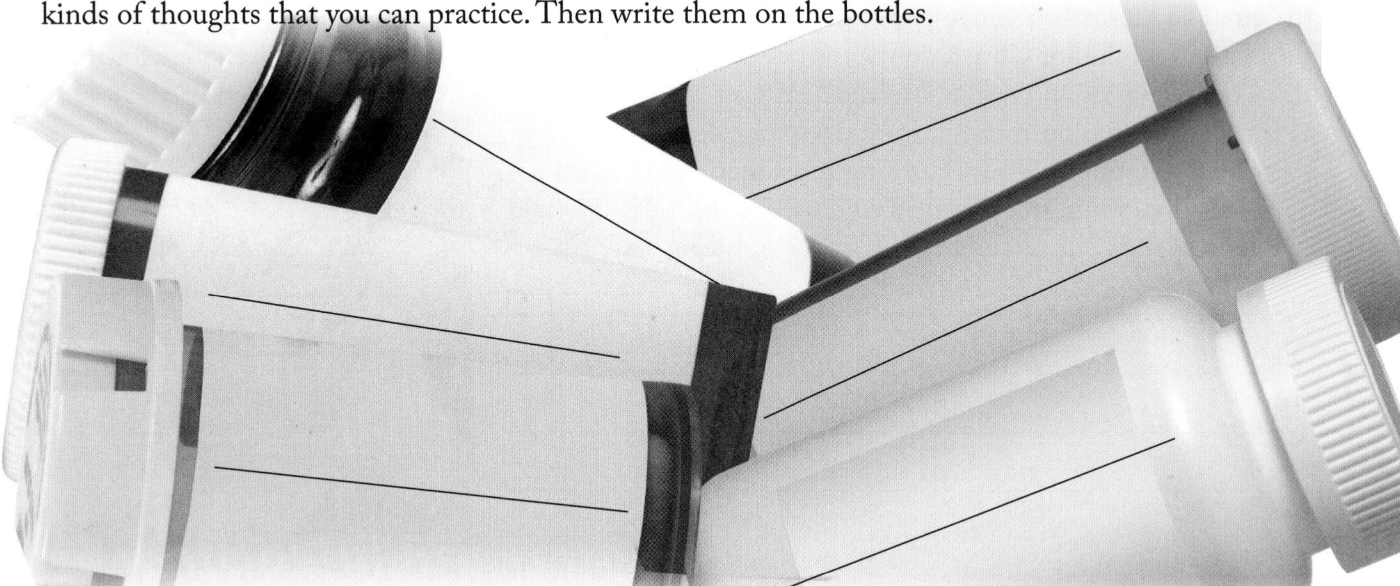

2. Your thoughts guide your words, goals, and actions. Read the Scriptures. List the main character, the thoughts that person may have had, and the effect those thoughts had on his or her outlook.

Reference	Character	Possible Thoughts	Effects
a. Genesis 39:21–23			
b. Ruth 2:17 and 4:13		followed Naomi, chose Naomi's God, accepted this as God's plan	
c. Acts 8:1–3			
d. John 21:7			later became humble and no longer impulsive
e. Acts 5:4–5 and 5:10		were greedy, looked for acceptance	
f. Daniel 1:8–9			served faithfully, promoted to governor

3. Choose a good type of thought from the bottles in Exercise 1. Describe how it could help you find contentment in a current difficult situation. Or tell how it could help you develop more Christlike character qualities.

a. the kind of thought ____________________

b. your explanation ____________________

Name ____________________

Colossians: Choices 22.1

Paul typically began his prayers with thanksgiving to God. Use Scriptures to find why thanksgiving should be expressed to God. Then complete Exercises 6 and 7.

1. Psalm 44:7a ____________________

2. Psalm 100:4–5

a. ____________________

b. ____________________

c. ____________________

3. Psalm 103:2–4

a. ____________________

b. ____________________

c. ____________________

d. ____________________

4. Romans 6:17–18 ____________________

5. Ephesians 1:6 ____________________

6. Why do you think giving thanks to God is a good way to begin a prayer?

____

____

7. Skim Colossians 1:3–14. Then name five things about the gospel that you are thankful to God for.
Dear God,
Thank you for

a. ____________________

b. ____________________

c. ____________________

d. ____________________

e. ____________________

Amen.

22.2 Colossians: Choices

Did you know that the Bible talks about a mystery? Paul wanted the Colossian Christians to understand it. Use the code to figure out what Paul taught about the mystery and its importance to Christians. Hint to use the code: Look at the letters and then count ahead (+) or count back (-) in the alphabet that number of letters. Then write the correct letter in the box. Finally, transfer boxed answers to the correct answer lines.

1. The mystery had been ____________ from ________ and ____________________, but would be made known to God's ____________. (Colossians 1:26) Remember, the Old Testament promised a New Covenant fulfilled through Christ's death and resurrection.

j h a e g r
-2 +1 +3 -1 -2 -4

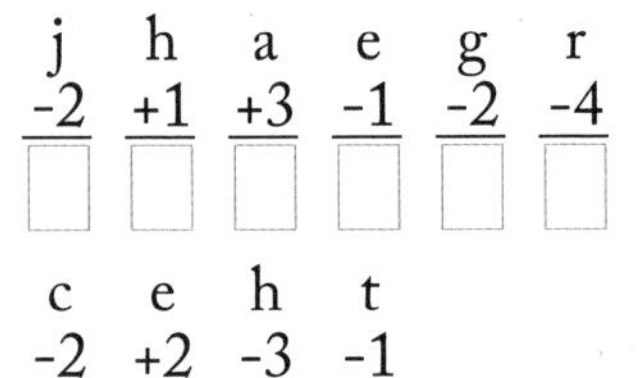

c e h t
-2 +2 -3 -1

e j o b o c u l n q u
+2 -5 -1 +3 +3 -2 -1 -3 +1 -3 -2

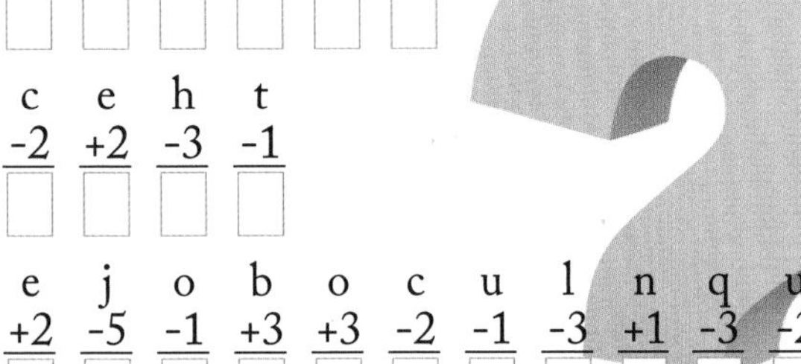

w b f k s t
-4 -1 +3 +3 +1 -1

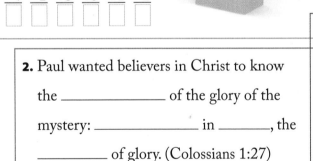

2. Paul wanted believers in Christ to know the ____________ of the glory of the mystery: ____________ in ______, the ________ of glory. (Colossians 1:27)

w e d k c r
-5 +4 -1 -3 +2 +1

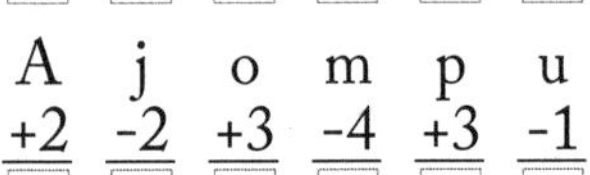

A j o m p u
+2 -2 +3 -4 +3 -1

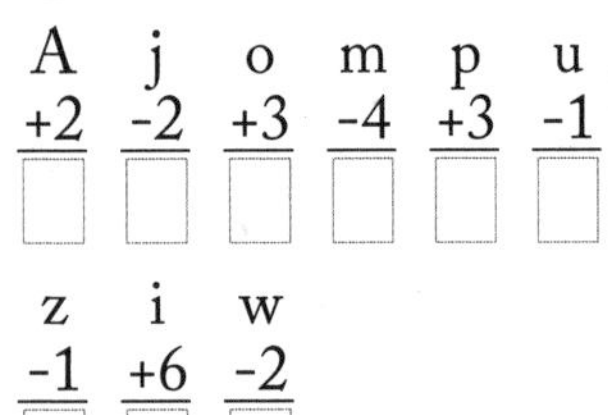

z i w
-1 +6 -2

k n o j
-3 +1 +1 -5

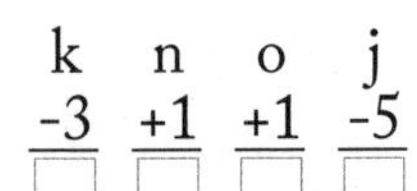

3. Paul explained that ______ the treasures of ____________ and ____________ are ____________ in Christ. (Colossians 2:2–3) Anyone wanting to know true wisdom needs to know Christ!

d i n
-3 +3 -2

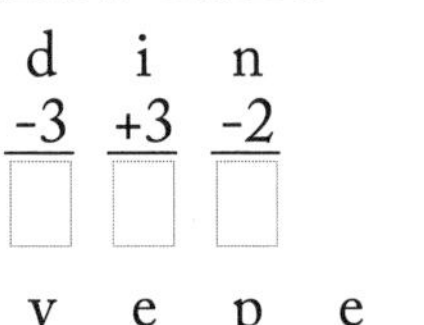

y e p e p i
-2 +4 +3 -1 -1 +4

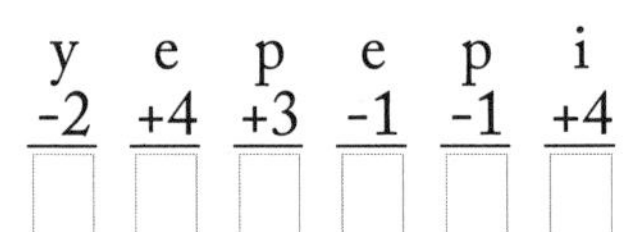

h m r z i f a f j
+3 +1 -3 -3 +3 -1 +3 +1 -5

e g f a i m
+3 +2 -2 +3 -4 +1

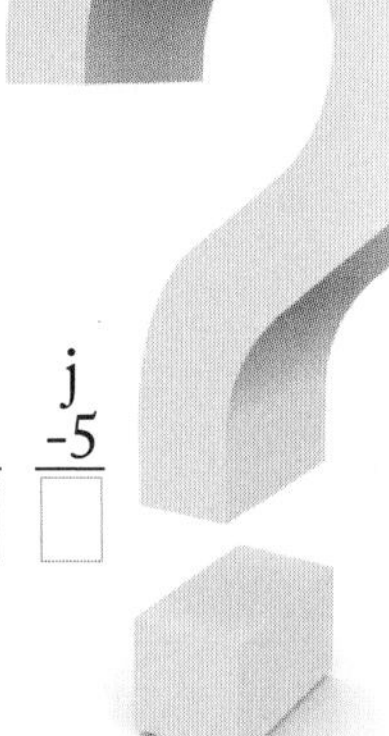

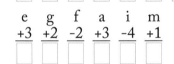

4. If you are a ________________ in Christ, then ______ are ______________ in ______! (Colossians 2:9) This truth is important for believers because all problems can be faced by knowing the all-powerful Son of God is present at all times through the Holy Spirit. Jesus has authority over everything!

a g i l f r d t
+1 -2 +3 -3 -1 +4 +1 -2

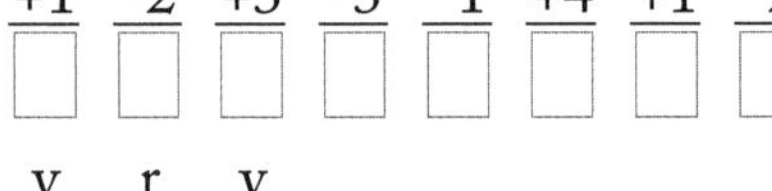

v r y
+3 -3 -4

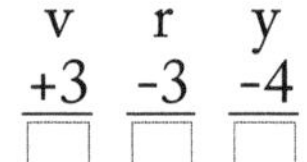

e m i s n g u b
-2 +2 +4 -3 -2 -2 -1 +3

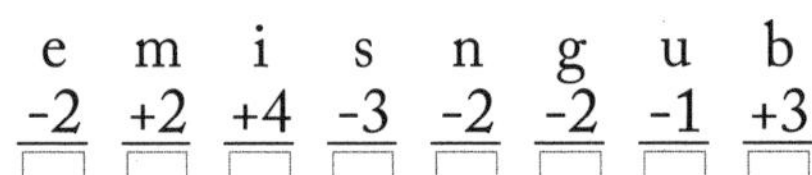

E k i
+3 -2 +4

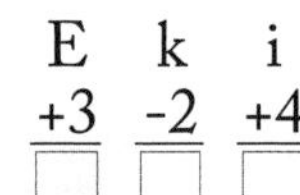

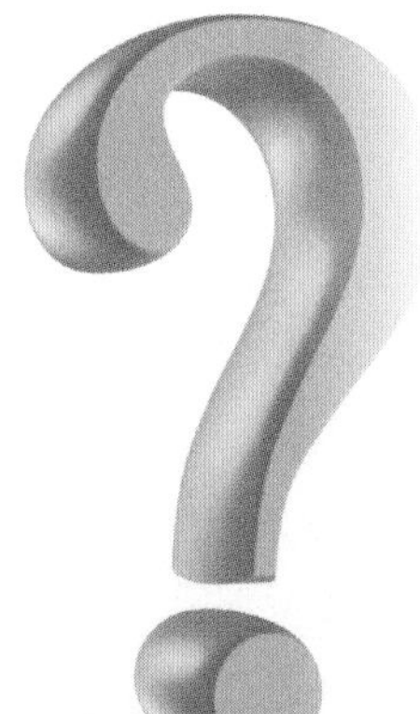

Name ______________________________

Colossians: Choices 22.3

1. Choose three traits from Colossians 3:12–14. Draw clothing on the hangers and label each piece of clothing with one of the three traits you want others to see you wearing.

a.

b.

c.

2. A Christlike lifestyle shows that Christ is the center of a person's life. Read Colossians 3:15–17 to discover some ideas to help you place Christ at the center of your life. Write the ideas on the lines.

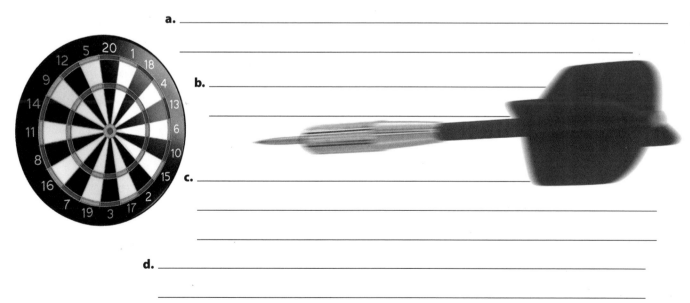

a. ______________________________

____

b. ______________________________

____

c. ______________________________

____

____

d. ______________________________

____

3. Paul told the Colossian believers that they should take off certain "clothing," clean it out of their wardrobe, and then put on new clothes. Take inventory in the closet of your heart. Pray and ask God to help you put on the godly clothes.

22.4 Colossians: Choices

1. Read the scenarios and explain how each person should respond in a way that glorifies God.

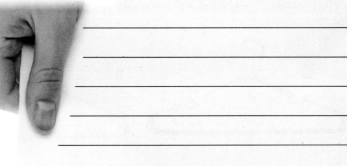

a. Kiley and Addison decide to go to the mall. While they are in the jewelry store, Addison notices that Kiley is putting a small pair of earrings in her purse while the clerk looks in another direction. Addison confronts Kiley about shoplifting, but Kiley just laughs and says that everybody does it. What should Addison do?

____

____

____

____

____

____

____

____

____

____

____

____

____

b. Hao has a broken leg. On his way to class he drops his notebook and cannot reach down to get it because of his cast. Michael sees what has happened. It is nearly time for the tardy bell, and Michael already has three tardies this month. If he stops to help Hao and is late for class, he will get a detention and miss football tryouts after school. What should Michael do?

2. Everyone lives under some kind of authority. Jesus' relationship to the Church provides the example that every relationship should follow to glorify God. Review Colossians 3:18–4:1. Then draw an arrow between people in relationship to each other. One match is done for you. On the arrows, write a responsibility each person has in that relationship. Two answers are provided.

CHRIST

SERVANTS/SLAVES (EMPLOYEES)

CHILDREN

WIVES

HUSBANDS

PARENTS

MASTERS (BOSSES)

CHURCH

(Arrow between CHRIST and CHURCH:) Christ loves and cares for the Church; the Church submits to the leadership of Christ.

Name ____

1–2 Thessalonians: Conduct

23.1

1. If a pebble is dropped into a pond or a lake, it forms ripples in the water that expand outwardly. One ripple causes another in an ever-widening circle. So it is with the gospel. In the ripples below, write the progression of the gospel from one believer to another. Use the references to find the name of these godly believers.

2. Use the references from 1 Thessalonians 2 to complete Paul's statements that show Paul as a good example to the Christians at Thessalonica. Use one word for each blank.

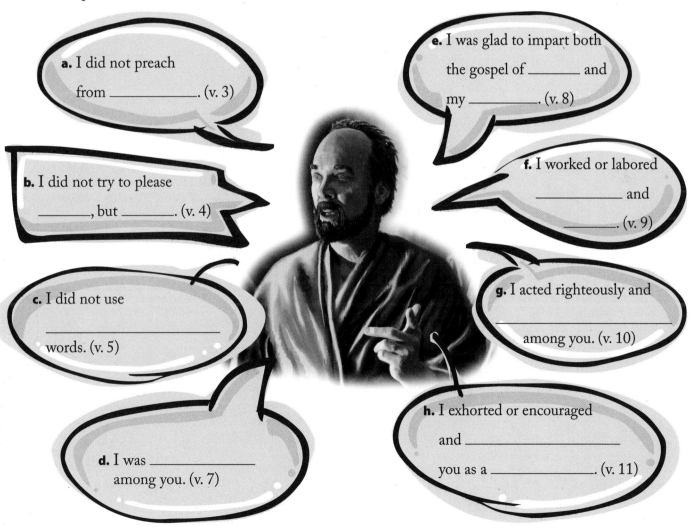

a. I did not preach from ______________. (v. 3)

b. I did not try to please ________, but ________. (v. 4)

c. I did not use ______________ words. (v. 5)

d. I was ______________ among you. (v. 7)

e. I was glad to impart both the gospel of ________ and my __________. (v. 8)

f. I worked or labored ______________ and __________. (v. 9)

g. I acted righteously and ______________________ among you. (v. 10)

h. I exhorted or encouraged and ____________________ you as a ______________. (v. 11)

3. Paul wanted the Thessalonian believers to live in a way that was worthy of God. Talk with a partner about a way sixth graders can be godly examples to others.

1–2 Thessalonians: Conduct

It feels good when someone encourages you. The Bible says Christians must encourage one another. Read 1 Thessalonians 5:11–25 and complete the chart.

	Reference	God commands me to ...	I can follow this command by ...
1.	v. 11	encourage others.	
2.	v. 12–13a	respect those in authority.	
3.	v. 13b		looking for ways to get along.
4.	v. 14	stand up for the weak.	
5.	v. 14		not getting frustrated when things do not go my way.
6.	v. 15	resist revenge.	
7.	v. 16	be joyful.	
8.	v. 17	pray all the time.	
9.	v. 18		remembering that God is the giver of all good things.
10.	v. 19	not quench the Holy Spirit or put out His fire.	
11.	v. 21		identifying what is good and always striving to do it.
12.	v. 22	avoid, or abstain from, evil.	
13.	v. 23–24	believe God is faithful to sanctify completely.	
14.	v. 25		praying for others and for myself.

Name ___________________________________

1–2 Thessalonians: Conduct 23.3

Paul did not want believers to be clueless about the second coming of Christ. Paul wanted them to be informed and prepared. Listed below are false ideas about Christ's return. Use the verses to match the falsehoods on the left with their associated truth on the right by writing the correct letter on the blanks.

1. ___ When a Christian dies, other Christians should be sad and should grieve the way unbelievers do. (1 Thessalonians 4:13)

2. ___ The Lord's return will be silent and in secret; no one will know. (1 Thessalonians 4:16)

3. ___ Christ's return should cause anxiety and fear for believers. (1 Thessalonians 4:18)

4. ___ Christ's return will bring peace and quiet to all. (1 Thessalonians 5:3)

5. ___ Christians can relax and do nothing but wait for Christ's return. (1 Thessalonians 5:6 and 5:8)

6. ___ Christians should fear God's wrath and judgment when Jesus returns. (1 Thessalonians 5:9–10)

7. ___ At the end, Earth will freeze and all life will die in deep, dark space. (2 Peter 3:10)

8. ___ Believers can know the exact time of Christ's return. (Matthew 24:36)

a. Believers should realize they are saved to live joyfully together with Christ forever.

b. Christ's return will bring sudden destruction with no escape for unbelievers.

c. Christians can have hope because of the Resurrection.

d. No one knows the day or the hour of Christ's return except the Father.

e. A shout, a voice, and a trumpet will loudly announce Christ's return for all to know.

f. Earth will be destroyed in intense heat and will burn up.

g. Believers should be comforted or encouraged when thinking of Christ's return.

h. Believers need to be alert and prepared with God's armor for His return.

Circle one of your favorite Bible truths about Christ's return above.

9. Tell a classmate why it is one of your favorites. Then discuss what your classmate circled and why.

23.4 1–2 Thessalonians: Conduct

In 2 Thessalonians, Paul addressed apostasy. He also challenged a disruptive believer. And he gave practical advice to the church for correct responses to the undisciplined in 2 Thessalonians 3:6–15.

1. Read the phrases. Consider whether they show a characteristic of a disciplined life or an undisciplined life. Then place a check mark under the correct heading to categorize the phrases.

Phrases	A Disciplined Life	An Undisciplined Life
• follow Paul's example		
• become a busybody		
• do no work at all		
• never grow weary in doing good or right		
• act disorderly or be idle		
• work to earn my own bread		

2. Connect the dots from problems among the Thessalonians to Paul's teaching on how to correct ungodly believers.

Thessalonian Church Problems	Paul's Teaching
Some were not obeying Paul's instructions. •	• Withdraw or keep away from them.
Some may have counted ungodly believers as enemies. •	• React to the disobedient so they feel ashamed.
Believers were being disorderly. •	• Admonish or warn the rebellious as brothers.

3. Unscramble the letters to complete the guideline that Paul gave about diligence. Explain the advice.

a. If a ________ will not __________, he shall ________ ________. (2 Thessalonians 3:10)
(anm) (rowk) (ton) (tea)

b. Why was this good, practical advice? ____

____

____

Name ______________________________

1–2 Timothy: Commitment

24.1

1. Paul wrote to give instructions about love and truth to his young friend Timothy. Read the verses to learn about Paul's godly advice.

a. From 1 Timothy 1:5, write inside the apple what the core of faith is. Write it again in the heart on the roots of the tree.

b. In the boxes, write three sources this core comes from.

c. Paul did not come up with the importance of love on his own. Jesus explained it in Mark 12:30–31. Whom did Jesus say you should love? Write the answer in the circles by the tree.

2. Finish the sentence by unscrambling the words.

Love is the __________
(TORO)

and love is the ___________.
(ITRUF)

3. Believers should be rooted in love and committed to truth. Use the letter box to discover, from 1 Timothy 1:13–16, the five truths Paul revealed about what Jesus had provided for him. Start at the letter shown under the answer lines and move one space up, down, or over as indicated by the arrow to discover each answer. Then write each correct letter on the lines.

C	N	E	R
V	A	T	H
M	Y	I	S
F	O	G	L

_ _ _ _ _
<Y ^T E> ^V vA

_ _ _ _ _
<O ^Y ^G A> vR

_ _ _ _ _
<L ^H <T <N N>

_ _ _ _
G> vY ^M N>

_ _ _ _
vS Y> vM <R

24.2 1–2 Timothy: Commitment

1. Godly leadership is described in 1 Timothy 3:1–10. Leadership qualities start with servanthood and include character, discipline, godliness, and contentment. Under each category, check all the phrases that describe each quality. Some will have more than one answer.

A. SERVANTHOOD
- ☐ loving toward God
- ☐ loving toward others
- ☐ greedy for power

B. CHARACTER
- ☐ quick to anger
- ☐ good leader of family
- ☐ used to rebellion from his children

C. DISCIPLINE
- ☐ steadfast in faith
- ☐ uncontrolled
- ☐ disciplined in truth

D. GODLINESS
- ☐ lacking in morals
- ☐ deep in convictions
- ☐ able to teach

E. CONTENTMENT
- ☐ greedy for money
- ☐ new in Christ
- ☐ blameless

2. You can be a young leader. Paul listed leadership qualities (1 Timothy 4:12). Match the qualities listed below to their correct description and picture. Note that the pictures show a young leader who demonstrates a particular way of being an example.

• **WORD** or **SPEECH** •
• **CONDUCT** or **LIFE** •
• **LOVE** •
• **FAITH** •
• **PURITY** •

What people hear me talk about shows my heart for God.

I care about people very much and want to show them God does too.

I will do right things out of a pure heart so God is honored and others see His righteousness in me.

How I live should attract others to Christ just by watching what I do.

I believe in Jesus. He changed my life. Others can see my trust in God.

3. Contentment is being satisfied with one's situation. Unscramble the words to discover what Paul said about it. Check your answer by looking up 1 Timothy 6:6.

_ _ _ _ _ _ _ _ _ with _ _ _ _ _ _ _ _ _ _ _ is great _ _ _ _.
(O D G S I N L E S) (N N O T C E M E T N T) (I G N A)

Name ______________________________

1–2 Timothy: Commitment

24.3

1. God never intended believers to have fear or timidity but to be bold in their faith. Finish the acronyms by using 2 Timothy 1:7 and Hebrews 13:6.

a. Describe the causes of fear.

b. Describe how you can show you are bold.

2. Second Timothy 2:1–7 gives examples of faithfulness. Fill in the blanks by following the color trail that matches each first letter. Then draw something in the colored boxes that will remind you of a way you can be faithful as the people mentioned are faithful.

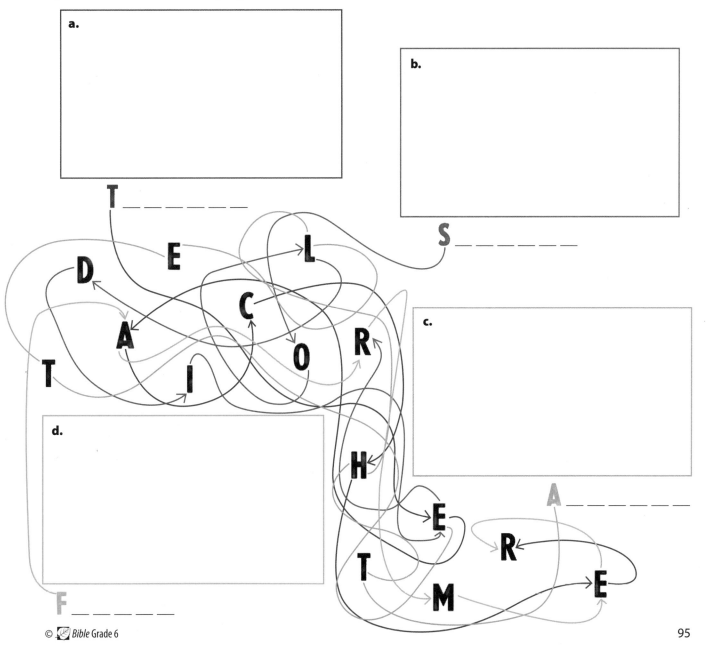

a.

T _ _ _ _ _ _

b.

S _ _ _ _ _ _ _

c.

A _ _ _ _ _ _ _

d.

F _ _ _ _ _

24.4 1–2 Timothy: Commitment

1. God's Word is central to starting well, growing in Christ, and finishing well as believers. Start with the second letter of the colored word codes in the clue boxes and cross off every other letter. Write the remaining letters on the lines. By doing this procedure, you will discover the four areas from 2 Timothy 3:16 that summarize the usefulness of the Bible for all areas of life.

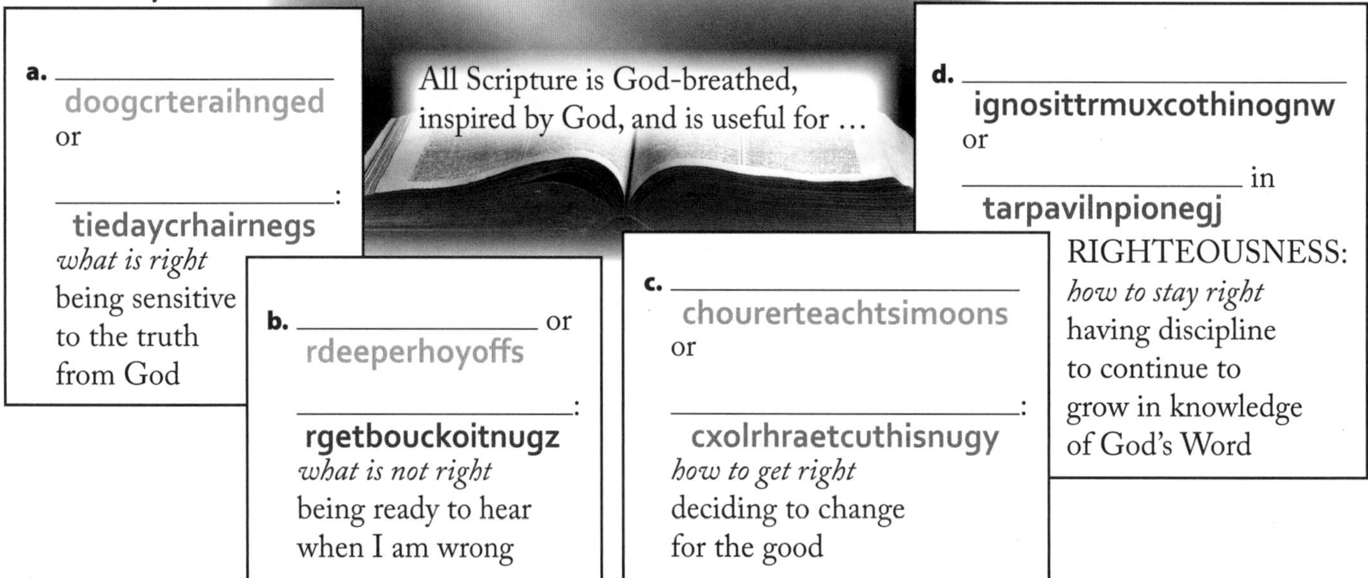

All Scripture is God-breathed, inspired by God, and is useful for …

a. ________________
doogcrteraihnged
or
________________:
tiedaycrhairnegs
what is right
being sensitive to the truth from God

b. ________________ or
rdeeperhoyoffs
________________:
rgetbouckoitnugz
what is not right
being ready to hear when I am wrong

c. ________________
chourerteachtsimoons
or
________________:
cxolrhraetcuthisnugy
how to get right
deciding to change for the good

d. ________________
ignosittrmuxcothinognw
or
________________ in
tarpavilnpionegj
RIGHTEOUSNESS:
how to stay right
having discipline to continue to grow in knowledge of God's Word

2. Cross off every other letter on the clues below to discover what will be the end result for a believer who follows God's Word. (2 Timothy 3:17) Then write your answer on the lines.

A believer will be ________________, ready for every ________ ________.
esqtubiepopsendz grotoads wiokruky

3. Sometimes it seems easier to give up when you are faced with a tough situation. But the Bible encourages believers to stay faithful! Read the scenarios and pretend you are giving advice to the person who wants to give up. Use the Scriptures to help form your answer and write it on the lines.

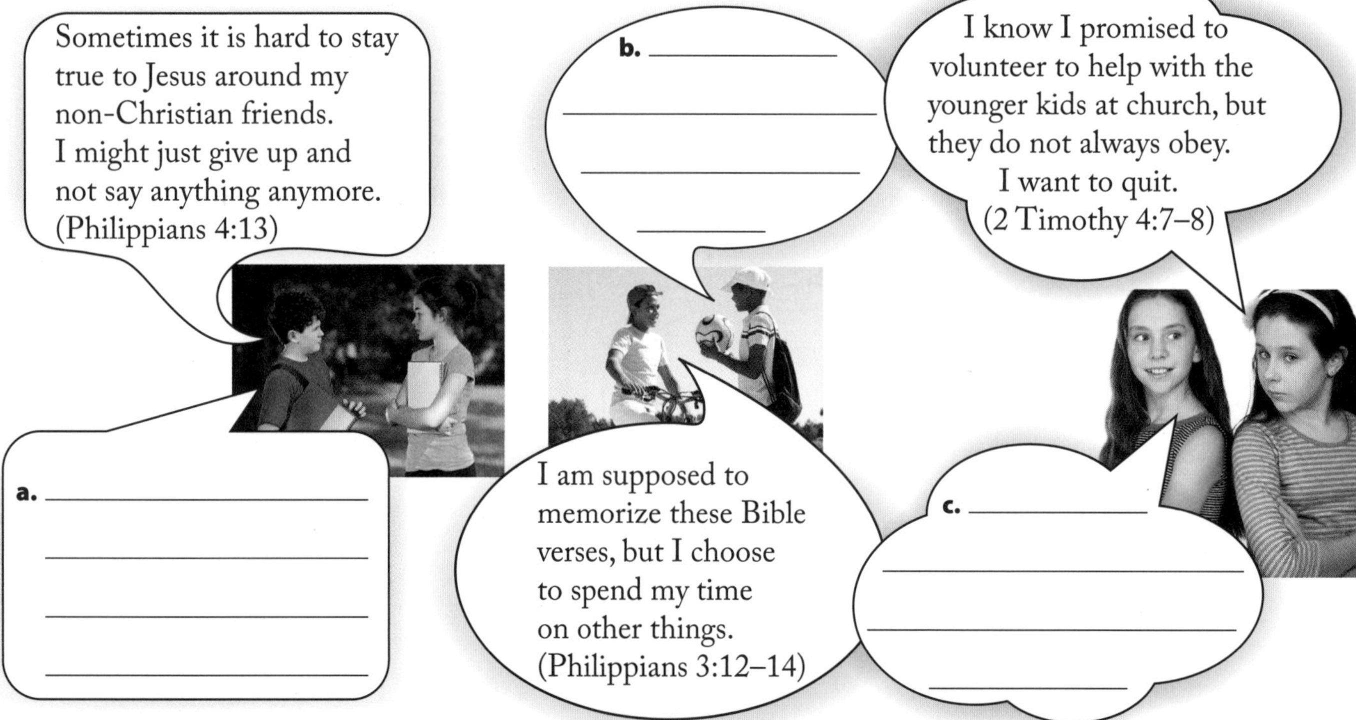

Sometimes it is hard to stay true to Jesus around my non-Christian friends. I might just give up and not say anything anymore. (Philippians 4:13)

a. ________________
____
____
____

I am supposed to memorize these Bible verses, but I choose to spend my time on other things. (Philippians 3:12–14)

b. ________________
____
____
____

I know I promised to volunteer to help with the younger kids at church, but they do not always obey. I want to quit. (2 Timothy 4:7–8)

c. ________________
____
____
____

Name ______________________________

Titus: A Healthy Church

25.1

1. Refer to Titus 1:1–2 to find what Paul told Titus to emphasize first to the Christians on Crete. Complete the sentences by writing the correct answer on the lines.

a. ____________ of God's elect or chosen + knowledge of the ____________ = ____________________. (verse 1)

b. God, who cannot ________, promised hope of ________________ __________. (verse 2)

2. Titus was God's ambassador, and he acted as Paul's representative. Because Titus had great ability, Paul gave him some important responsibilities. Read the Bible passages to discover where Titus went and why he went. Fill in the blanks. On the map, circle each city or area mentioned.

a. Titus went with Paul to ____________________ as an example of the gospel being preached among ____________________. (Galatians 2:1–2)

b. Titus went to ____________________ to help with the relief fund for the Judean ____________________. (1 Corinthians 16:2–3, 2 Corinthians 8:16–19)

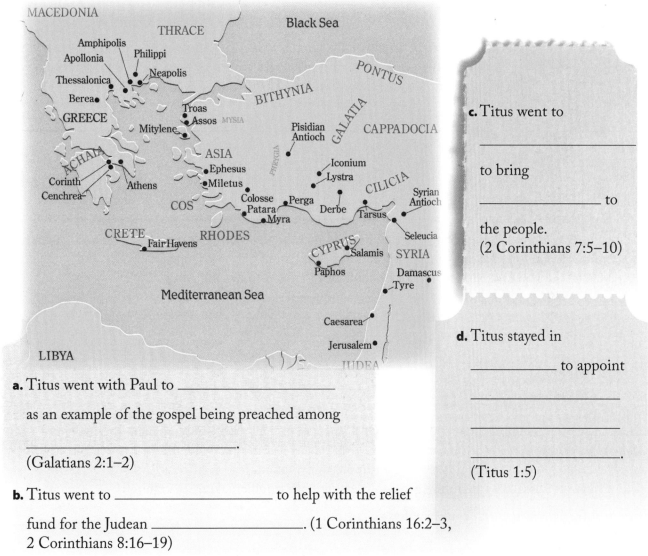

c. Titus went to ____________________ to bring ____________________ to the people. (2 Corinthians 7:5–10)

d. Titus stayed in ____________ to appoint ____________________ ____________________ ____________________. (Titus 1:5)

3. Ability leads to responsibility. Titus was given responsibility because of the unique abilities he had. Write one ability God has given you. Then list what responsibility that gives you.

25.2 *Titus: A Healthy Church*

1. The first step in having a godly character, which includes having a good reputation, is to know good from evil. Read the phrases and check the box indicating whether they are good or evil.

GOOD	EVIL	
☐	☐	**a.** obeying my parents
☐	☐	**b.** lying
☐	☐	**c.** gossiping about someone
☐	☐	**d.** serving others
☐	☐	**e.** defending the powerless
☐	☐	**f.** having fits of anger

2. One way to grow in godliness is to be trustworthy when relating to your parents at home. When your parents can trust you, you will have access to certain privileges and responsibilities. Think through ways to be trustworthy and what might result. Then fill in the chart.

What helps your parents trust you?	*What privileges and responsibilities may result?*

3. Your reputation is a reflection on your character. How others see you is often a result of who you are on the inside. List one part of your reputation that you would like to change. Then list what your new reputation could be. Include changes you could start in order to develop your new character.

One Part of Current Reputation to Change

____

New Reputation

____

I will change!

I will show these changes:

a. __________________________

b. __________________________

c. __________________________

4. Your reputation is influenced by your friends. Titus had to deal with troublemakers in the church just as you may have to deal with troublemakers. Find out what the apostle Paul told Titus about dealing with such people by reading Titus 3:10. For more information, read Matthew 18:15–17. On the blueprint, write the steps Scripture gives for dealing with troublemakers in a church.

Blueprint for Dealing with Troublemakers

a. ____

b. ____

c. ____

d. ____

Name ______________________________

Titus: A Healthy Church 25.3

1. Titus had to start from the beginning to teach the Christians at Crete how to be an effective church. Refer to Titus 2:1–8. In the Church at Crete chart, list the descriptions that the groups within the church at Crete were supposed to fulfill. Then think about your church. Choose some of Paul's advice that could be used by the same groups of people in your church. Write godly advice in the appropriate section for your church today.

Church at Crete

My Church

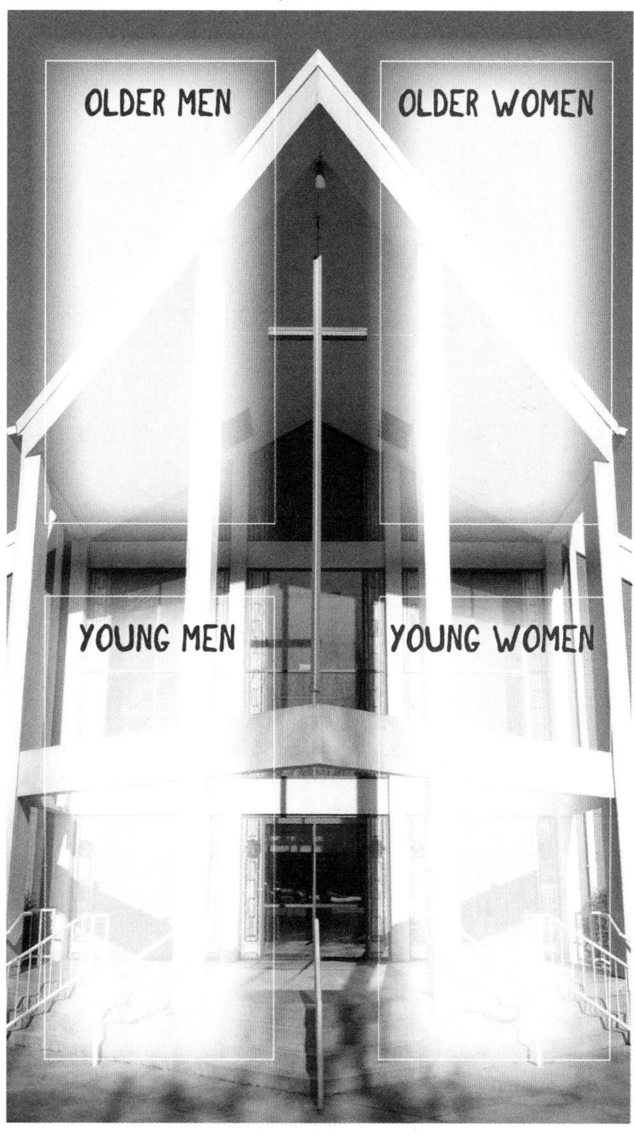

2. Refer to Titus 2:5–15. Then circle a thumbs-up if the advice agrees with biblical truth and a thumbs-down if it does not.

a. Following the truth of God's Word produces a genuine life.

b. Living a godly life gives your enemies much to blame you for.

c. When you follow sound doctrine, others are drawn to Christ by observing you.

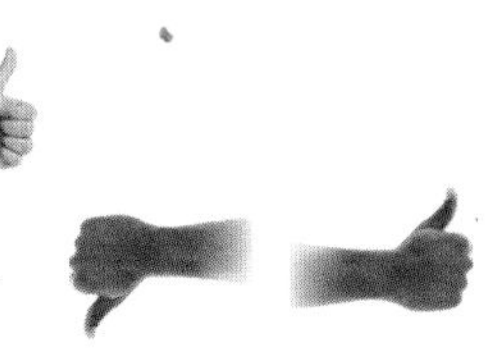

25.4 Titus: A Healthy Church

1. The Bible is full of men and women who grew in spiritual maturity and who changed drastically because of their walk with God. Paul was changed from a Pharisee who tried to kill Christians into an apostle of the gospel. And Peter was changed from someone who denied Christ into a bold evangelist. Both grew in their spiritual walk. Write three ways you can grow spiritually as they did.

a. ______________________________

b. ______________________________

c. ______________________________

2. Paul encouraged Titus to teach how to build a strong, unified church. A strong church results when each believer puts off negative attitudes and divisive behaviors and puts on unifying and loving traits. Cross out the attitudes and behaviors believers should put off. Circle those that they should put on.

gossiping about each other

praying for people, even when they are unkind

lashing out at others when angry

seeing the good in people

making fun of people

being kind

getting easily irritated

helping people who need it

picking out the bad in people

respecting and obeying authority

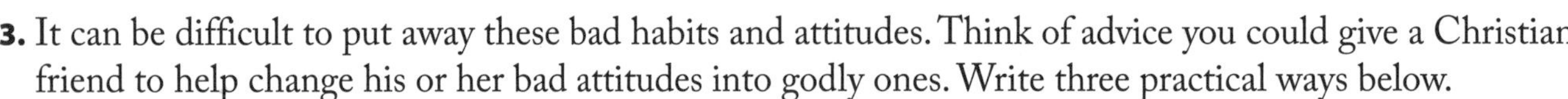

3. It can be difficult to put away these bad habits and attitudes. Think of advice you could give a Christian friend to help change his or her bad attitudes into godly ones. Write three practical ways below.

a. ______________________________

b. ______________________________

c. ______________________________

Name ______________________________

Philemon: Forgiveness 26.1

1. Use the Word Bank and the book of Philemon to fill in Paul's letter with the correct words. (Hint: Not all the words in the Word Bank will be used.)

DEAR PHILEMON,
I THANK GOD FOR YOU AND FOR THE CHURCH THAT MEETS IN YOUR HOME. GUESS WHO I MET HERE IN ROME? YOUR SLAVE ONESIMUS! GREAT NEWS—HE'S A CHRISTIAN NOW!
I'M SENDING HIM BACK TO YOU, HOPING YOU WILL ____________ HIM. AS AN APOSTLE, I COULD ORDER YOU TO ____________ ME, BUT INSTEAD I AM ASKING YOU TO SHOW FORGIVENESS TO ONESIMUS BECAUSE YOU ____________ ME AND GOD. YOUR ____________ AND TRUST IN GOD, SHOWN THROUGH OBEDIENCE, WILL BETTER YOUR ____________ WITH ONESIMUS AND ALSO WITH GOD!

YOUR BROTHER IN CHRIST,
PAUL

Word Bank

rejoice	peace	discipline
obey	relationship	faith
forgive	love	

2. Pretend that you are Philemon and it is now six months after Paul wrote to you. What would you tell Paul about your current relationship with Onesimus? What would you say about the request Paul had made in his letter to you? Write your response to Paul.

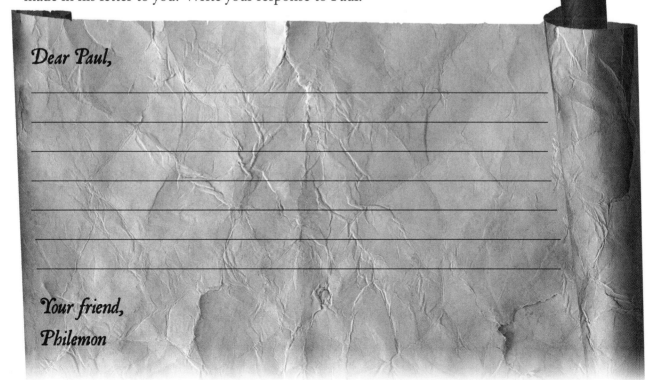

26.2 Philemon: Forgiveness

Having had the authority of an apostle, Paul could have ordered Philemon to accept Onesimus back as a brother in Christ. Instead, Paul chose a different way—an appeal through love rather than one based on authority and demands. Answer the questions and follow the directions.

1. According to John 15:17, why should Christians appeal through love? ______________________

____

2. What does an appeal through love show others? ______________________

____

3. Rate the following appeals. Circle 👍 if the response shows a good way to make an appeal. Circle 👎 if the response shows a poor way to make an appeal.

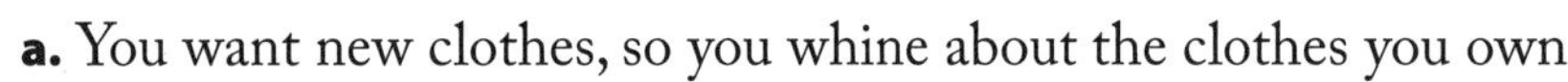

a. You want new clothes, so you whine about the clothes you own.

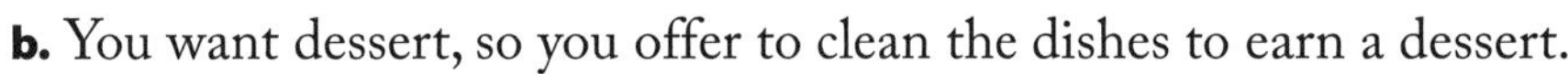

b. You want dessert, so you offer to clean the dishes to earn a dessert.

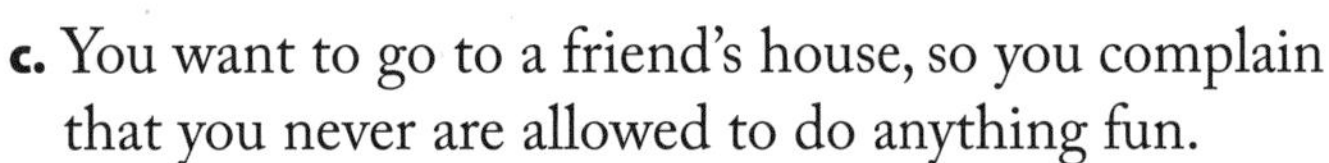

c. You want to go to a friend's house, so you complain that you never are allowed to do anything fun.

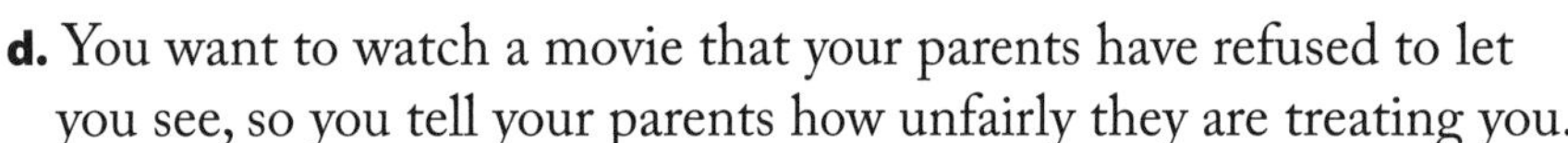

d. You want to watch a movie that your parents have refused to let you see, so you tell your parents how unfairly they are treating you.

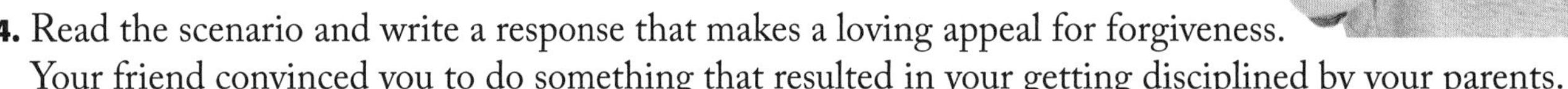

4. Read the scenario and write a response that makes a loving appeal for forgiveness. Your friend convinced you to do something that resulted in your getting disciplined by your parents.

____

Read the scenarios and look up the references. On the mirror, write a key word or phrase from the verse that would reflect God's love in each situation.

5. Ethan borrowed Heath's MP3 player to listen to some songs at home. Ethan's little sister accidentally stepped on it and broke it. Ethan told Heath it would take him a couple of months of doing extra chores to save up the money to replace it. How should Heath act toward Ethan? (Colossians 3:13)

____

____

____

____

6. Jenni's mom has been fighting a serious illness for several months. At first, her friend Joy listened when Jenni needed to talk. But now Joy is tired of hearing about Jenni's worries. How can Joy find encouragement to keep on being a compassionate friend? (Galatians 6:2)

Name ______________________________

Philemon: Forgiveness 26.3

1. An online payment is used to pay for a service or a product or to pay off debt. When Paul offered to pay anything that Onesimus owed Philemon, it was as if he was making an online payment to Philemon's account. Fill in the first payment statement to show what Paul offered Philemon for restoration with Onesimus. Fill in the second payment statement to show what Jesus offered to God for you.

Online Payment — RESTORATION BANK

Name:	
Date:	60–61 AD
Pay to:	
Amount:	
Memo:	for any debt of ...

Online Payment — RESTORATION BANK

Name:	
Date:	33 AD
Pay to:	
Amount:	sacrifice of My life
Memo:	for salvation of ...

2. Forgiving others is a commandment. Not forgiving brings serious consequences, such as bitterness, attacks from Satan, and no forgiveness of personal sins, to the believer. Christians have been forgiven a debt they could not repay, therefore Christians need to forgive others. Remembering the debt that they have been forgiven makes it easier to forgive those who have wronged them! Use the coordinates to find the alphabet letter that fits the code.

Code Box

	5	6	7	8
1	e	g	t	l
2	i	v	r	n
3	m	a	s	h
4	o	c	f	p

When I ___ ___ ___ ___ ___ ___ ___ ___
(4,8)(2,7)(3,6)(4,6)(1,7)(2,5)(4,6)(1,5)

___ ___ ___ ___ ___ ___ ___ ___ ___ ___ ___, I realize how much deeper my
(4,7)(4,5)(2,7)(1,6)(2,5)(2,6)(1,5)(2,8)(1,5)(3,7)(3,7)

___ ___ ___ ___ ___ ___ ___ ___ ___ ___ ___   ___ ___   ___ ___   ___ ___ ___ ___ ___ ___
(2,5)(2,8)(3,8)(1,5)(2,7)(2,5)(1,7)(3,6)(2,8)(4,6)(1,5) (2,5)(3,7) (2,5)(2,8) (4,6)(3,8)(2,7)(2,5)(3,7)(1,7)

and how much ___ ___ ___ ___ ___ ___   ___ ___ ___   ___ ___ ___ ___ ___ ___ ___ ___   ___ ___!
(4,6)(3,8)(2,7)(2,5)(3,7)(1,7) (3,8)(3,6)(3,7) (4,7)(4,5)(2,7)(1,6)(2,5)(2,6)(1,5)(2,8) (3,5)(1,5)

26.4 Philemon: Forgiveness

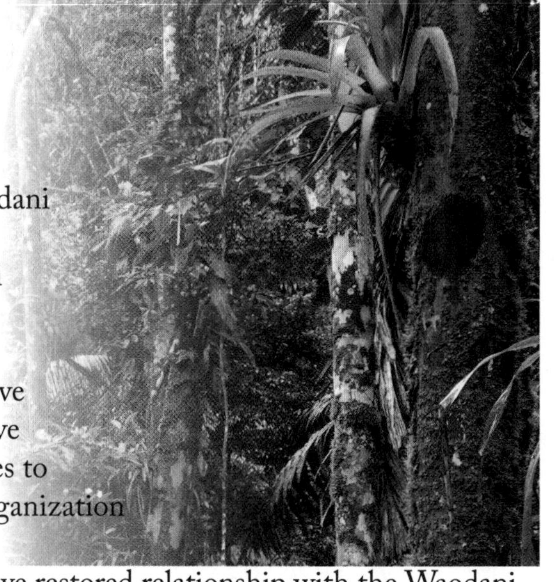

When Nate and Marj Saint moved to the Amazon jungle, they raised three children. One of them, Steve, was barely five years old when his dad was killed by the Waodani people. At age nine, Steve visited Rachel, his aunt, and lived in a Waodani village. He played and hunted with the children, learning the language and the culture. He ended up with adopted Waodani "grandparents" and loved being part of the Waodani's church. Steve listened to his mother and aunt pray for and love the Waodani, so it never occurred to him to hate them. When Steve had grown up, the Waodani invited him to come back. So Steve moved his wife and their four teenagers from the United States to live with this tribe in the jungles of Ecuador. He started an organization that develops new technology to help tribes like the Waodani.

1. Unscramble words to find key concepts that helped Steve have restored relationship with the Waodani.

a. VEIRGOFNESS ____________________

b. VELO ________

c. YEPARR ___________

2. Imagine how hard and unlikely it would have been for Steve to forgive the Waodani people. Some of your relationships might be difficult, or maybe you need to start some new friendships. Use the unscrambled words above to write a sentence explaining how you could restore or build a relationship.

a. ____

b. ____

c. ____

Unlikely relationships can be developed through Christ. Unlikely relationships existed in Paul's time as well as today. Jesus breaks down walls of separation between God and people and between people and others through the salvation He provided.

3. Use Colossians 3:11 and 3:23–24 to explain, in the left-hand column, Paul's instructions about how to handle new relationships. In the right-hand column, describe how these sample principles can be put into action to mend relationships that have been damaged because of cultural or social issues in today's world.

First-Century World	Today's World

Name ________________________________

Hebrews: Growing in Faith

1. The author of Hebrews explained that Christ is superior to all other people and all practices and systems. Christ is the most important, highest, and best in comparison to everyone and everything in the Old Covenant, specifically. Decode these words related to the Old Covenant by dropping two letters and unscrambling the rest. Check your answers by looking up the Hebrews references.

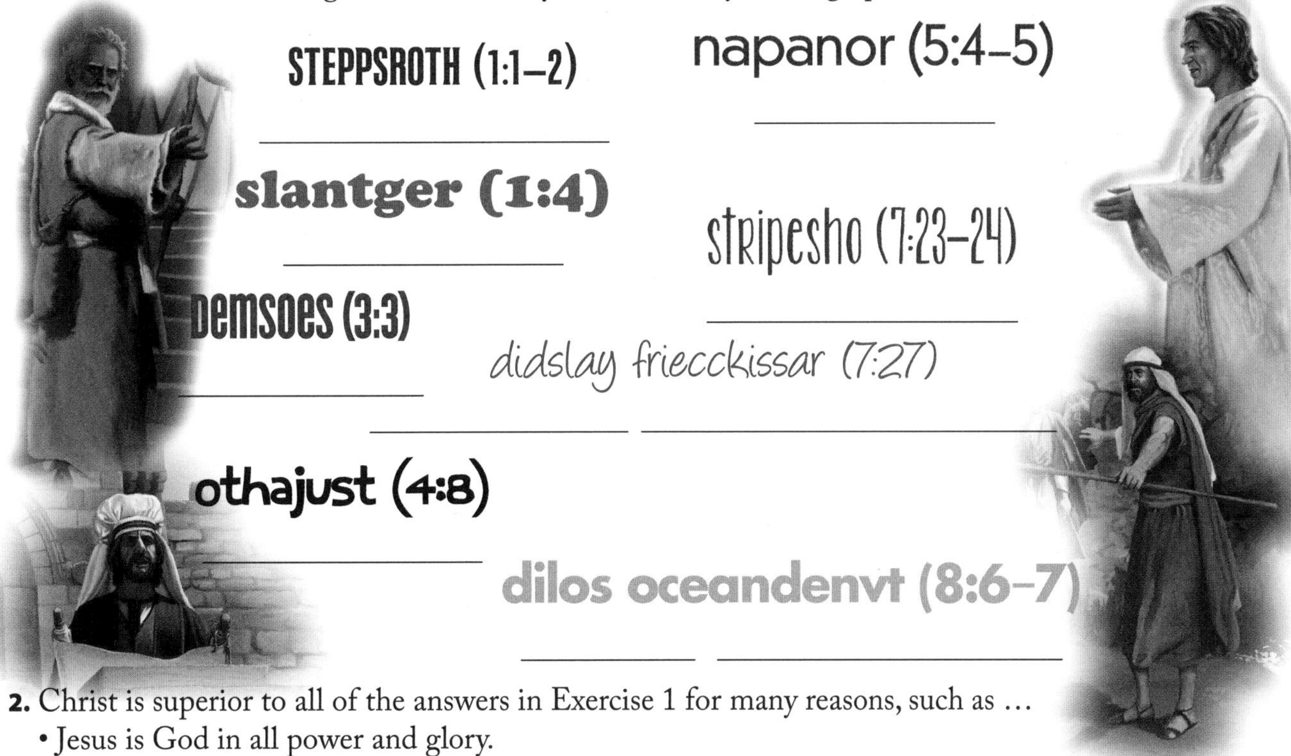

2. Christ is superior to all of the answers in Exercise 1 for many reasons, such as …
   - Jesus is God in all power and glory.
   - He sits on the throne in heaven.
   - He understands believers and their weaknesses.
   - He is praying for believers.
   - He completely saves people.

   Draw a picture or sketch stick figures that will help you remember Christ's superiority.

27.2 Hebrews: Growing in Faith

1. God made two covenants with people. The new one, mediated by Jesus, is superior to the old one. Decide whether the phrases below are part of the Old Covenant or the New Covenant. Draw an arrow to the old-fashioned typewriter if the sentences refer to the Old Covenant. And draw an arrow to the new laptop computer if they refer to the New Covenant.

• God's promise is fulfilled through the sacrifice of Jesus. •

• God makes promises to Abraham and his descendants. •

• God changes people on the inside, giving them a new heart. •

• There is freedom and power in Christ to obey from within. •

• People need to keep all the commands in the Law. •

• The gift of grace is given to all who ask for it. •

• Priests continually make sacrifices. •

• There is no need for guilt or shame. •

• People can have faith in Christ's work on the cross, not their own work. •

• All can become an equal part of God's family. •

• God's love selects a specific group of people from which the Messiah will come. •

• God's chosen nation waits for a future promise. •

• God's love is shown to all people through the Savior. •

• Promises from God involve animal sacrifices and obedience from people. •

• God puts His laws in people's mind and writes them on their heart. •

2. Compare Jeremiah 31:31–34 with Hebrews 8:7–12. Then circle the element of the New Covenant above that is mentioned in both of these passages. Take time to thank God for the better covenant!

Name ___

Hebrews: Growing in Faith

27.3

1. Your faith response reveals your level of confidence in God, His character, and whether you believe He will accomplish what is best for you. Having no faith can change to hope and can grow to trust and then to active faith. Give yourself an honest assessment. On each line, place an **X** along the line to indicate your level-of-faith response.

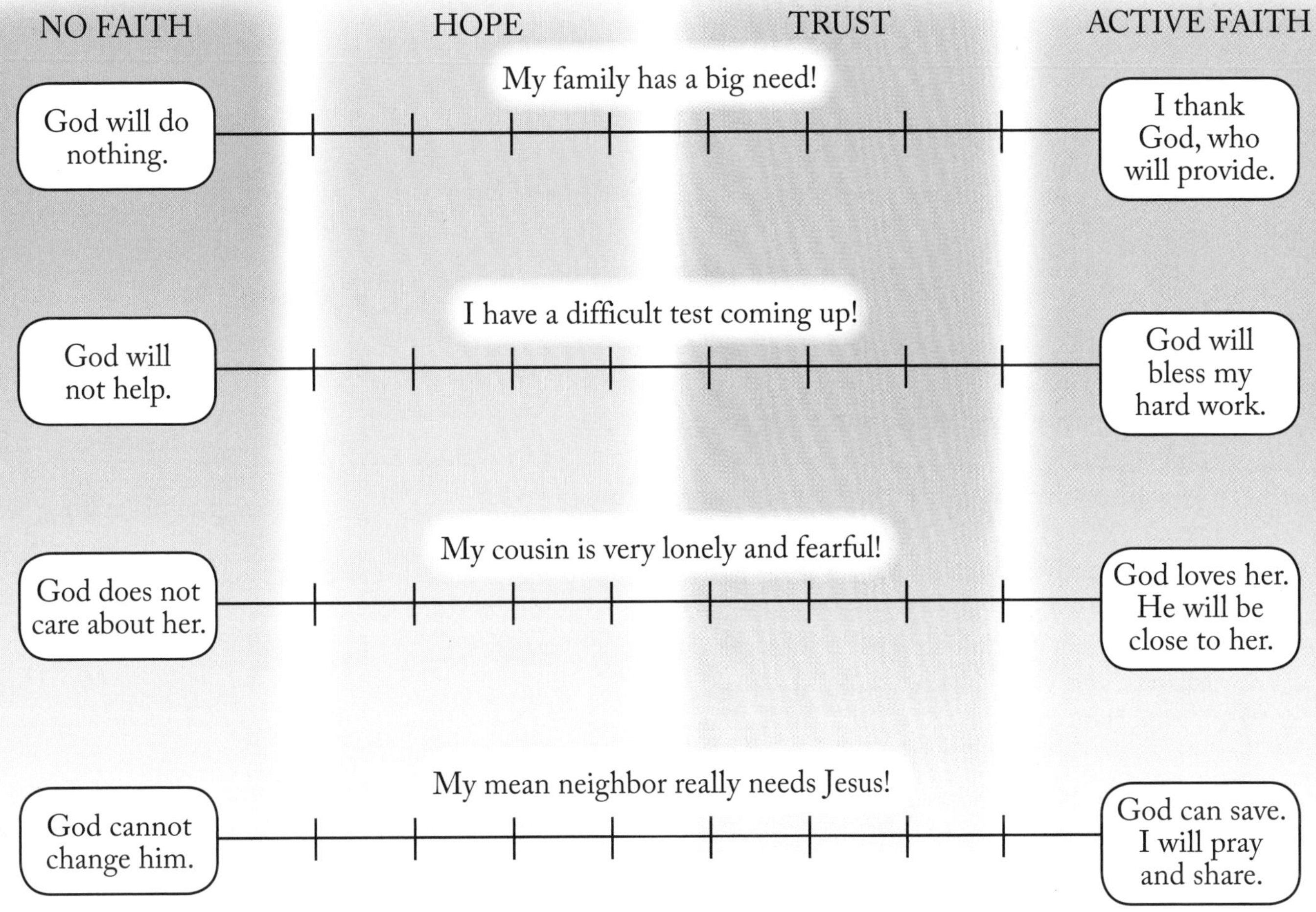

NO FAITH
HOPE
TRUST
ACTIVE FAITH
My family has a big need!
God will do nothing.
I thank God, who will provide.
I have a difficult test coming up!
God will not help.
God will bless my hard work.
My cousin is very lonely and fearful!
God does not care about her.
God loves her. He will be close to her.
My mean neighbor really needs Jesus!
God cannot change him.
God can save. I will pray and share.

2. Your faith should always be growing. Think about your overall level of faith. Consider whether it is most often at the no-faith, hope, trust, or active-faith stage. Add your name or a classmate's on the student-name blank below. Then describe how you or a classmate has shown active faith.

By faith, ___ proved faith in action by ___
(student name)

___

___

___

___

___

___.

27.4 Hebrews: Growing in Faith

Read Hebrews 12:10–11. Discipline can come from outside or inside. From outside, it can come from a parent, a teacher, or God. When discipline comes from inside, it is called **self-discipline** or **self-control**. First, without looking up any Scriptures, try placing on the blanks the letter of the correct answer to the clues. Next, read the Scriptures for any clues that you were not at first able to match and then complete the exercise.

Clues

___ **1.** the theme of Hebrews 11–13 (Hebrews 11:6)

___ **2.** another word for self-control (Hebrews 12:11)

___ **3.** something you need to be in order to grow in self-control (Hebrews 12:11)

___ **4.** someone to look to for growing in faith and self-control (Hebrews 12:2)

___ **5.** a word that describes God and gives a reason to believe in Him (Hebrews 12:22)

___ **6.** something people should do out of joy and obedience (Hebrews 12:28)

___ **7.** a type of motivation to do the right thing that comes outside myself

___ **8.** a type of motivation to do the right thing that comes from inside me

___ **9.** an action that students should do in relation to leaders, parents, teachers, and God (Hebrews 13:17)

___ **10.** an important goal for people who are living the Christian life (Hebrews 13:5)

___ **11.** a word that tells how long Jesus will remain the same (Hebrews 13:8)

Answers

a. faith

b. living

c. trained

d. external

e. serve or worship

f. obey

g. chastening or discipline

h. Jesus

i. contentment

j. forever

k. internal

12. Test yourself against these ways of acting in faith that are mentioned in Hebrews 12–13. On each spiral, mark how close you think you are to the center of internal self-control.

• praying

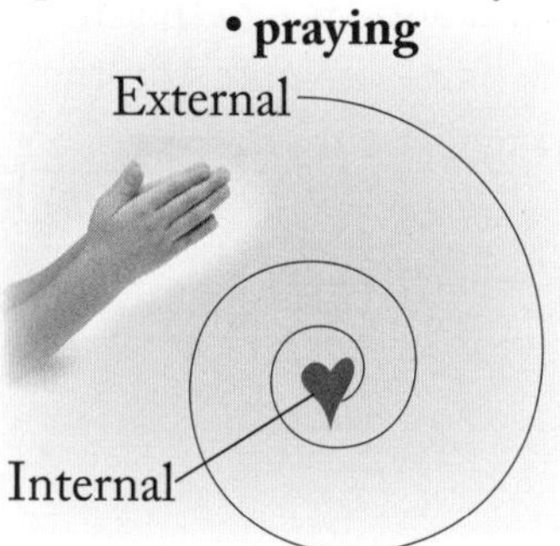

• doing what is right

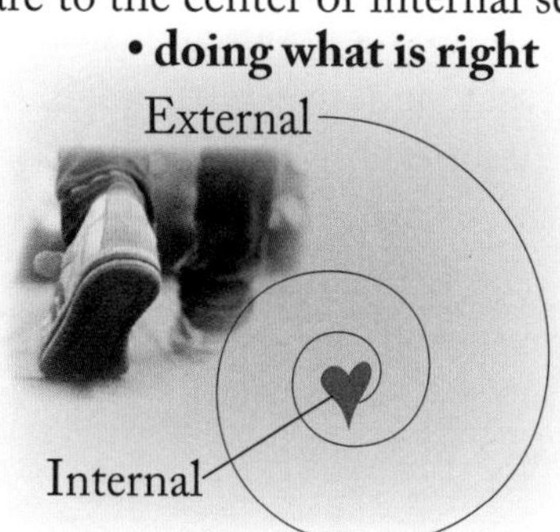

• obeying authority

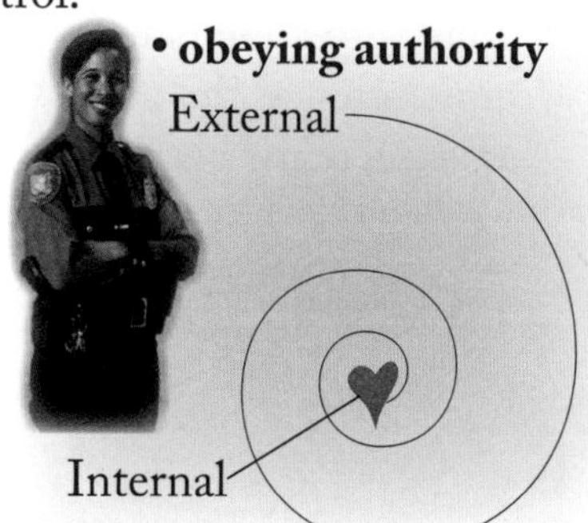

13. Read Philippians 1:6 and 2:13 and Hebrews 12:2. Then, write inside the key-chain tag the key to maintaining self-control. (Hint: The answer is a name.)

Name ______________________________

James: Trials 28.1

1. James the half brother of Jesus had a unique family tree. Use Mark 6:3 to fill in James' family tree.

2. Read the verses. Then answer the questions in complete sentences and follow the directions.

a. How did James feel about his older brother? (John 7:3–5)

____

b. What probably changed his thinking? (1 Corinthians 15:7)

____

3. Persevering in faith through a trial brings you closer to God. Cross out every other word to learn more about God's relationship with you during any trial. Look carefully to see which of the first two words begins the correct answer, and write the true statement on the blank.

The I believer can is recognize able that to God solve is the with problem. me.

____

God I is can watching see me God's to power catch by anything His I mighty do protection that of is me. wrong.

____

4. Summarize James 1:2–4 as an imaginary post on a social-networking site. Draw in a profile picture and use 140 characters or less for your message.

28.2 James: Trials

1. God's logic for how to go through trials is not the same logic as the world has. Do the math to figure out the missing words in God's logic. Write the correct word answer (next to the correct number answer in the Word Bank) on the lines. (Hint: You will not need to use all the words in the Word Bank.)

Word Bank

trusting (21)
listening (18)
submitting (27)
truth (17)
obeying (16)
faith (19)
wisdom (20)
patience (25)
growing (24)

Step 1: God's Word is ________ ($28 \div 7 + 13$).

Step 2: ________ ($3 \times 8 - 6$) to God is the way to learn ________ ($15 \div 3 \times 4$).

Step 3: When a believer knows and listens to the truth, ________ ($14 - 5 \times 3$) to God during the trial shows ________ ($3 \times 11 - 9$) ________ ($20 \div 4 + 14$)!

2. Read the scenarios and the Scriptures. Write a response that shows the person in the scenario listened to God's wisdom and did not doubt God's truth.

a. Paul's favorite band is coming to town, and Paul really wants to see them in concert. However, he does not have the money. One day as he is getting ready for school, he notices that $20 has fallen out of his dad's pocket, and it is lying on the bathroom floor. His dad probably would not notice if Paul took it so that he could go to the concert. How would Paul handle this situation if he were to use godly truth and wisdom? (Mark 14:38)

____

____

____

b. Lisa is staying at a friend's house for a birthday slumber party. Her friend Anna suggests that they watch a PG-13 movie. Lisa's parents do not let Lisa watch those movies. But Lisa knows that this is Anna's party, and she does not want to cause a problem by being the only one who cannot watch the movie. How can Lisa handle this situation in a godly way? (1 Corinthians 10:13)

____

____

____

____

Name ______________________________

James: Trials 28.3

1. James 1:14–15 details the progression of temptation. Fill in the blanks. The first letter of each answer has been provided.

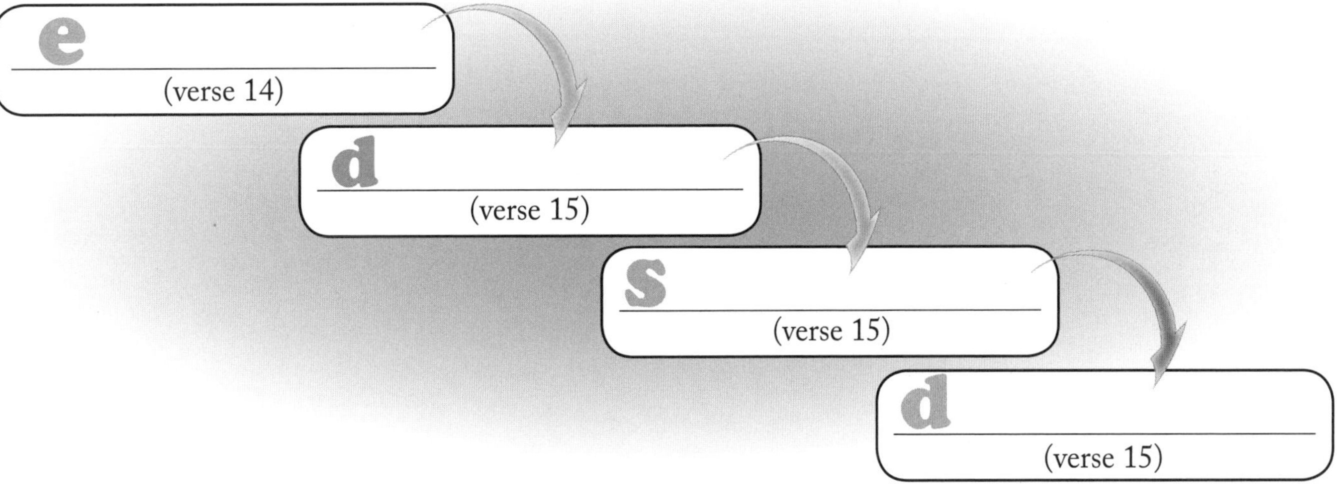

2. Temptation has occurred since the first people lived on the earth. Even Jesus was tempted. Use the Scriptures to answer the questions on the chart.

	Genesis 3:1–7	Matthew 4:1–11
Where did the temptation take place?		
Who was involved?		
What temptation represented the lust of the flesh?		
What temptation represented the lust of the eyes?		
What temptation represented the pride of life?		
What protection against temptation was available? Was it used effectively?		
What was the result?		

3. Consider how the Matthew 4 passage in Exercise 2 can help you when you are tempted. Then spend time praying, writing, or drawing whatever will help you remember this passage during times of temptation.

28.4 James: Trials

1. James described someone who looks in the mirror, sees his or her dirty face, and then walks away without washing it. Read the verses in Proverbs and mark each bar of soap with either an asterisk (*) or an **X**. Put an * if the verse tells qualities that will help make your appearance pleasing to God. And put an **X** if the verse states characteristics that should not be in your life.

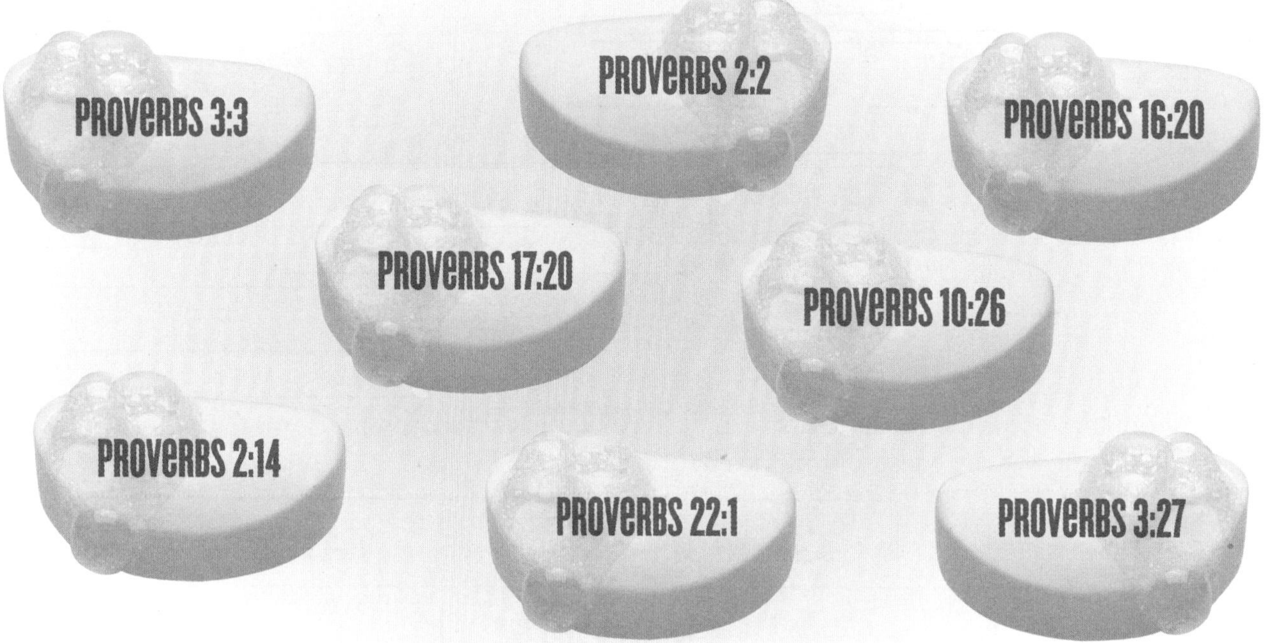

James 1:22 reminds Christians to be doers of the Word and not hearers only. Write what you or your church family could do to demonstrate being a doer of the Word in the situations below. Then follow the directions in Exercise 4.

2. Dmitri's family is going through a trial. His father just came home from the hospital and needs constant care. The family needs to hire a nurse, or else his mother will have to give care 24 hours a day. She has two small children to care for also. Dmitri's family needs help.

____

____

3. Mrs. Lopez has a hard time taking care of her home since her husband died. She has been a faithful member of the same church for 50 years and has helped many others. Now she needs help.

____

____

4. Write a summary of the first chapter of James.

____

____

____

____

Name ____

Easter 29.1

The triumphal entry introduced Jesus as King. Here are some statements describing events surrounding this time. They contain underlined errors. To make the statements true, change the false parts by writing the correction on the lines. Refer to John 11 and 12 to check your answers.

1. Before the triumphal entry, Jesus did sermons and banquets in His last travels around the region.

____

2. When Jesus raised Zacchaeus from the dead, the religious leaders plotted to kill only Zacchaeus.

____

3. Caiaphas the high priest gave an unintentional prophecy about Jesus. Caiaphas declared that two men must die for the Romans.

____

4. One surprise at the triumphal entry was that Jesus rode a stallion and people shouted, "Hallelujah."

____

5. Another surprise was the title the crowd gave Jesus—Savior and Messiah.

____

6. Hundreds of years ago, the prophet Isaiah prophesied that Jesus would enter Jericho on a donkey.

____

7. Jesus came to serve and give His life as a payment for many! If needed, read Philippians 2:5–11 to help you unscramble the clues. Then fill in the five circle sections showing how Jesus demonstrated service, love, and sacrifice and what the result of His sacrifice will be.

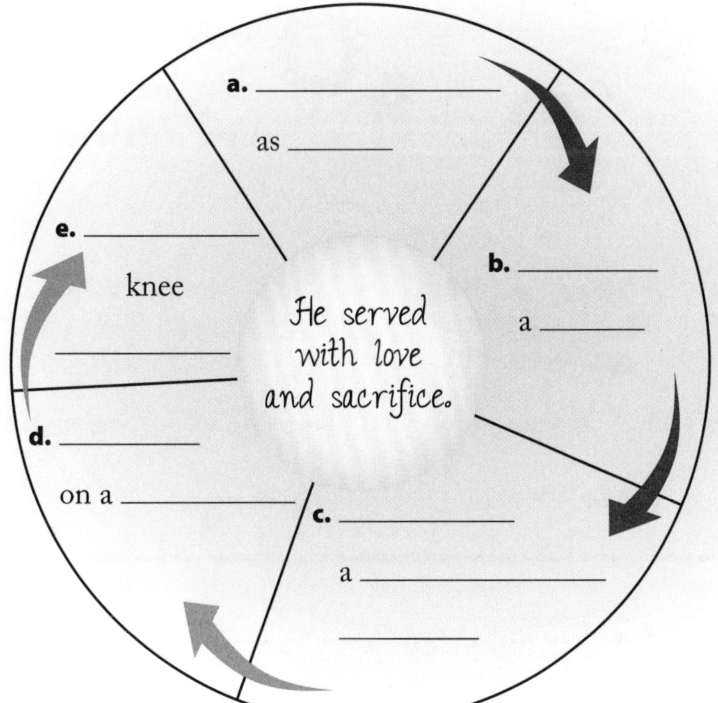

Scrambled Clues

a. **sixteed** as **odG**

b. **robn** a **anm**

c. **ldevi** a **slesisn file**

d. **ided** on a **srocs**

e. **yeevr** knee **owbde**

29.2 Easter

1. The Bible declares that love is the primary quality believers should show. They can show love in selfless service to others. Match the sentences in the Bad Attitudes column to an opposite Good Service sentence by correctly drawing lines to connect the dots.

BAD ATTITUDES			GOOD SERVICE
a. I always have to clear the dirty dishes. Let someone else do it.	●	●	I will take care of my things and organize my room properly.
b. Clean up after the dog? Ugh! I did that last month. Why me again?	●	●	If I can help with the dishes, or anything else, I will.
c. My room is fine. Clean it up? I will just close the door.	●	●	I will always do the best I can in my studies and everything else.
d. I do okay in school without trying. Why try harder? It really does not matter.	●	●	My dog is my responsibility; I will do the cleanup and walk him too.

2. Mitch is thinking of ways to serve. He thought of areas of service but needs help in knowing what to do to serve. Write suggestions in the thought bubbles to show how Mitch could serve others well.

3. Prayer is an important part of a believer's life. Rate yourself on your prayer life by putting an **X** along the line to indicate where you are.

I never pray.	*I seldom pray.*	*I sometimes pray.*	*I often pray.*	*I pray about everything.*

4. How could you develop a better prayer practice? ______________________________

____

Name ______________________________

Easter 29.3

Refer to Philippians 2:3–8. Complete the sentences by circling the correct word.

1. Before being born, Jesus existed as (God / an angel / nothing).

2. At His crucifixion, Jesus' physical body died because He was (deity / human / bad).

3. Jesus showed total (humility / knowledge / cowardice) because He allowed Himself to be (corrupted / crucified / comforted).

Follow the directions.

4. Why did Jesus choose to die instead of calling on God the Father to rescue Him? (Matthew 20:28)

____

____

5. Think about what it means to serve. Use at least four words to name characteristics of serving and create a crossword out of them. An example is given for you.

6. At the Crucifixion, Jesus demonstrated complete submission to His Father. Write about something else Jesus did that showed submission to God the Father and tell why, in your opinion, Jesus did it.

____

____

____

____

29.4 *Easter*

1. Listed below are eight events that occurred during the last days of Jesus' life on Earth. Number them in order from 1 to 8.

___ Jesus was arrested, and Pilate ordered Jesus to be whipped. Soldiers then mocked Jesus with a crown of thorns and a purple robe.

___ The stone was rolled away, and there was an empty tomb because the Lord had risen!

___ Jesus was nailed to a cross between two thieves. The sign over the cross said "This is Jesus, the King of the Jews."

___ Crowds shouted "Hosanna!" and welcomed Jesus as King of Israel by waving palm branches.

___ Jesus used bread and wine at the Last Supper to help the disciples remember His death.

___ Jesus was buried.

___ Judas betrayed Jesus in the garden.

___ A soldier gave Jesus vinegar on a sponge before Jesus announced, "It is finished!" Then another soldier thrust a spear into the body of Jesus, showing He was dead.

The empty tomb and the ascended Lord changed every believer's life. In the Code Box, move one box up, down, left, or right from the letter given to discover each answer. Write the correct letter on the blanks to reveal words describing results of the resurrection of Jesus and His ascension into glory.

Code Box				
R	J	C	D	O
H	A	F	L	B
U	T	N	E	G
W	Q	S	P	X
M	I	V	K	Y

2. Jesus is not here; He is ___ ___ ___ ___ ___!
^H vQ <P vL >T

3. Jesus is the ___ ___ ___ ___ ___ ___ Lord!
vD <V >I >M ^S vB

4. Jesus has ___ ___ ___ ___ ___ ___ ___ ___ ___ death and hell.
<D >D vF >W vH ^P <J <G >C

5. A believer's sins are ___ ___ ___ ___ ___ ___ ___ ___.
<L ^B <J vB >M <K <G vF

6. A believer is set ___ ___ ___ ___ from sin's control.
<L ^H >N vL

7. God gives all believers ___ ___ ___ ___ ___ and ___ ___ ___.
>S <G vJ ^F >N ^A >D vX

8. Every believer has ___ ___ ___ ___ ___ ___ ___ ___ ___ ___ ___.
^P vA >N ^H ^S <F vD <B vQ >A <G

9. The Holy Spirit fills every believer with ___ ___ ___ ___ ___ to ___ ___ ___ ___ ___ ___ ___.
<X ^B ^M vL <J vU >M ^Q <E ^P vN >Q

10. Jesus will ___ ___ ___ ___ ___ ___ someday.
^H >N >U <T <J vF

Name ___

James: Perseverance

James 2:1–13 teaches about showing favoritism on the basis of how much money a person has. Read the statements. Circle **T** if the statements are true, according to the Scripture passage. Circle **F** if the statements are false and rewrite those on the lines to make them true.

1. Believers should show favoritism. **T / F**

___

2. Showing favoritism is not a sin. **T / F**

___

3. At church, preference should not be given to people on the basis of what they wear. **T / F**

___

4. God gives the poor the opportunity to be rich in faith and to be heirs of His kingdom. **T / F**

___

5. God says that judgment triumphs over mercy. **T / F**

___

6. Read James 2:21–25 (and skim Joshua 2, if needed) to discover why Abraham and Rahab are mentioned in the New Testament. Write an **X** on the blanks beside the person about whom the statements are true. (Note: One or more statements might be true of both people.)

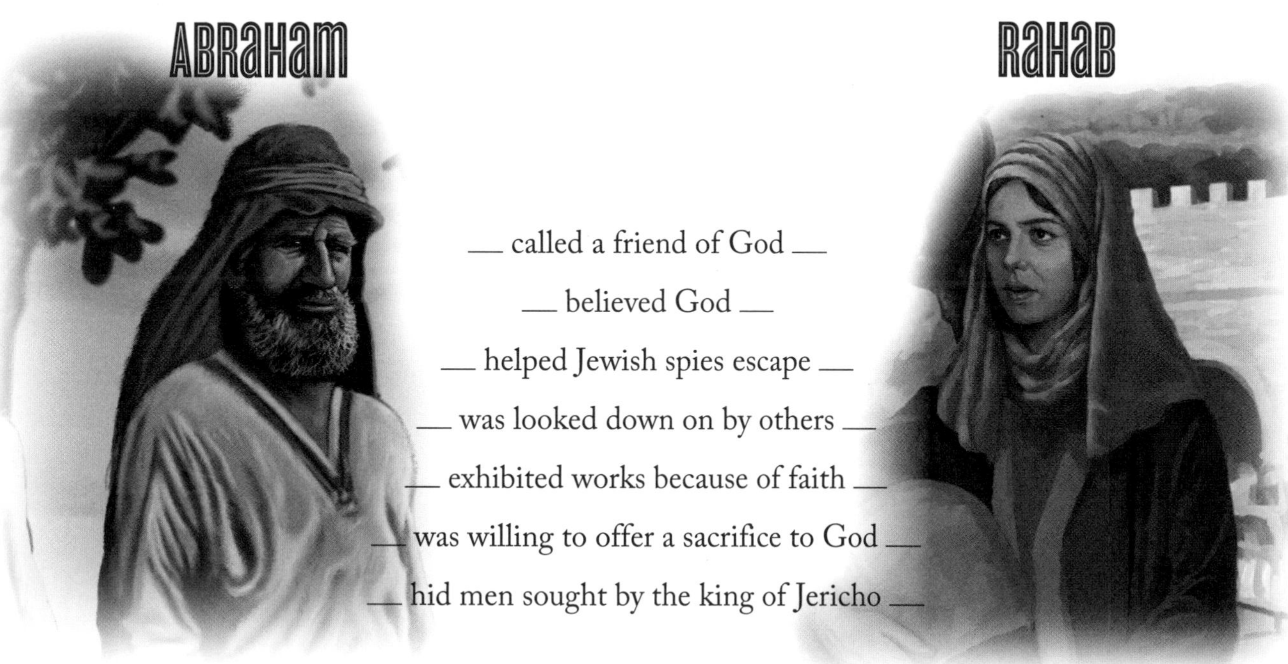

ABRAHAM
RAHAB
__ called a friend of God __
__ believed God __
__ helped Jewish spies escape __
__ was looked down on by others __
__ exhibited works because of faith __
__ was willing to offer a sacrifice to God __
__ hid men sought by the king of Jericho __

7. Describe how faith and works are related on the basis of the answers in Exercise 6.

___

30.2 James: Perseverance

James understood the power of the tongue, for good and for evil. He used word pictures to give understanding of that power. Refer to James 3:1–8. Draw in a picture frame each of the four things to which he compared the tongue. Also write each thing on the lines.

The tongue is like …

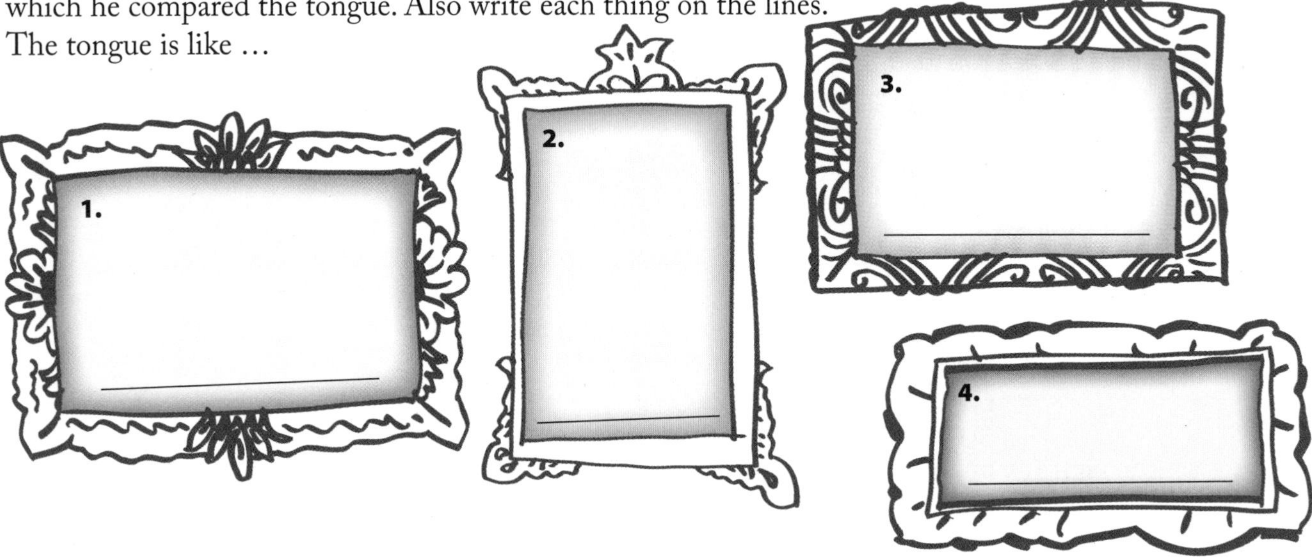

Believers need perseverance to control their tongue. Work with a partner and write one verse from Proverbs that gives good advice to help you remember to control your tongue. Then work together to create a new proverb that gives good advice to sixth graders about their speech.

5. Advice from Proverbs: ______________________________

____

6. New sixth-grade advice: ______________________________

____

7. Read the speech balloons. These students need to show self-control in their speech. Rewrite the conversation to show words that would be pleasing to God.

Name ____

James: Perseverance 30.3

1. Look up James 4:1–2. Sort the letters by color and then unscramble them to make words. Write the correct word on the matching colored lines.

The book of James says fights and arguments come from _ _ _ _ _ _ _ _ _ that _ _ _ _ _ _ _ from _ _ _ _ _ _ _ _.

E R T A S I S B E L H I W T D N E T I

2. Faith perseveres without pride or judgment. James 4:7–12 tells how to avoid fights and quarrels caused by selfish desires. Following this biblical advice makes everyone a winner. Write three ways you can submit to God and two ways to resist the devil.

SUBMIT TO GOD

SUBMIT TO GOD

RESIST THE DEVIL

3. Read Diana's e-mail to her Christian school teacher. Write a response that her teacher might send to remind Diana of what James 4:13–5:6 says.

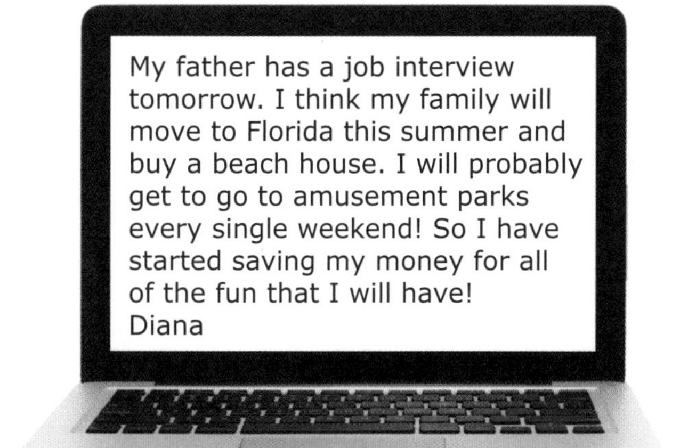

My father has a job interview tomorrow. I think my family will move to Florida this summer and buy a beach house. I will probably get to go to amusement parks every single weekend! So I have started saving my money for all of the fun that I will have!
Diana

30.4 James: Perseverance

1. Work with a partner. Read each game space. Then refer to James 5:7–20 and write the correct verse number on the blanks to match the teaching from James to the game-board sentences.

2. Now play this game with your partner. Think about the advice the book of James gives in these verses on prayer, praise, and staying faithful.

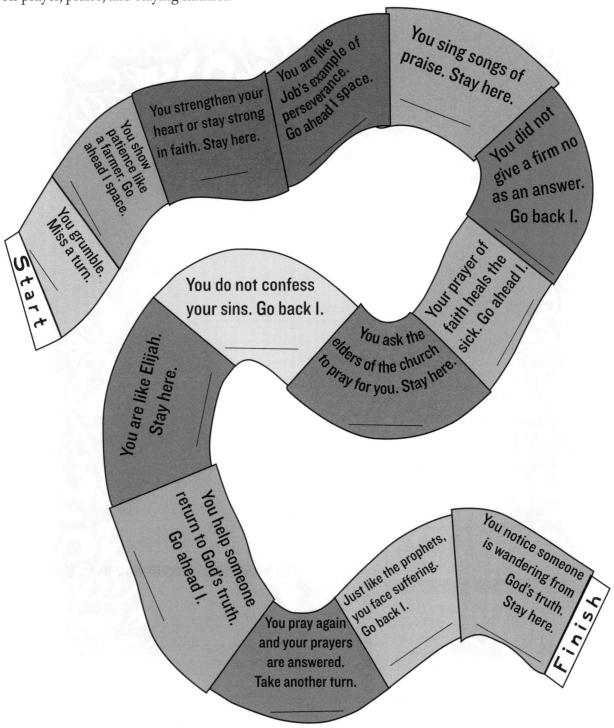

Start

You grumble. Miss a turn. ____

You show patience like a farmer. Go ahead 1 space. ____

You strengthen your heart or stay strong in faith. Stay here. ____

You are like Job's example of perseverance. Go ahead 1 space. ____

You sing songs of praise. Stay here. ____

You did not give a firm no as an answer. Go back 1. ____

Your prayer of faith heals the sick. Go ahead 1. ____

You ask the elders of the church to pray for you. Stay here. ____

You do not confess your sins. Go back 1. ____

You are like Elijah. Stay here. ____

You help someone return to God's truth. Go ahead 1. ____

You pray again and your prayers are answered. Take another turn. ____

Just like the prophets, you face suffering. Go back 1. ____

You notice someone is wandering from God's truth. Stay here. ____

Finish

Name ______________________________

1–2 Peter: Service and Growth

31.1

1. Look up the verses to fill out the paperwork for Peter's student ID.

School: The King's School

Class year: 64–65 AD

Name given at birth: ____________ (Matthew 10:2)

Name given by Jesus: ____________ (Matthew 10:2)

Brother's name: ______________ (Matthew 10:2)

Friend like a brother: __________ (2 Peter 3:15)

Job: ______________________ (Mark 1:16)

Current job: evangelist, apostle

Accomplishments:

Literary: I wrote two letters in the New Testament: ________________ and ________________. (2 Peter 3:1)

Spiritual: I was given a new name when I stated Jesus is _______ ______________. (Matthew 16:15–16)

Experiential: One time I was so excited about seeing Jesus that I ______________ _____ ____________. (Matthew 14:28–29)

Educational: To teach me to accept everyone in the Body of Christ, God gave me a vision. In it, He told me to eat ________________ ________________. (Acts 10:9–15)

2. Just as an earthly prince or princess represents his or her country, a believer represents the King and His whole royal family. Peter wrote about how God's children, as part of a royal priesthood, should act and think. Find each answer by filling in the missing vowels. Look for clues in these verses: 1 Peter 1:13–16, 1:22, 2:1, and 2:17.

B__ s__lf-c__ntr__ll__d.

B__ h__ly.

G__t r__d __f m__l__c__, d__c____t, h__p__cr__s__, __nv__, __nd wr__ng w__rds.

L__v__ y____r br__th__rs __nd s__st__rs __n Chr__st.

H__n__r y____r l____d__rs.

31.2 1–2 Peter: Service and Growth

A college student named **Taylor**, a sojourner for Jesus, spent a month in Mongolia. He traveled with a United States team to take the gospel to nomadic herders in the countryside. A Mongolian Christian named **Ganaa** helped the team. Follow Taylor's microblog. First, underline unique elements of the Mongolian nomadic culture. Then, circle ways Taylor and Ganaa were ambassadors for Christ as they followed the teachings in 1 Peter 2.

Taylor **July 15**
Arrived safely in Mongolia! Getting to know my team and so grateful for my new Mongolian Christian friend, Ganaa. We have been praying together!

Janie **July 16**
Good to hear! Keep me informed. Praying for you and your team and Ganaa.

Taylor **July 18**
Way out in the countryside visiting herders in their **gers**, meaning **felt tents**. Herders move their sheep, goats, cows, and yaks around each season.

Taylor **July 21**
Nomadic families do everything alone since they are so far from a town. Every day, my team helps a family milk their 40+ goats and make curds and yogurt.

Janie **July 22**
Wow! Interesting experiences. Did you eat the yogurt?

Taylor **July 24**
Yes, eating yogurt and getting good at playing kid games with sheep knucklebones! Also teaching kids English. Love it!

Taylor **July 29**
Cool! Today Ganaa and I shared with a whole family the Bible truth of Jesus as the Good Shepherd who knows His sheep. Now they want Ganaa to start a Bible study! www. BibleGateway.com

---

Joseph **August 1**
Answers to prayers abound! E-mail me more pictures, okay?

Taylor **August 2**
Will do, Joe. Ate goat BBQ and drank hot sheep milk today! Ganaa said I was a humble servant in Jesus to do it with a smile, but not easy at all. Glad it encouraged Ganaa and others, though.

Taylor **August 9**
Many Mongolians pray to items from nature at a rock pile. So we taught about Jesus as the Creator of nature, the Cornerstone, and the Rock of Ages! Sad to be leaving.

Taylor's Dad **August 11**
Will be at airport to pick you up. Cannot wait to hear more!

Name ______________________________

1–2 Peter: Service and Growth

31.3

Read the scenarios. Draw in the circle a smiley face if the people serving are motivated to bring glory and honor to God. Or, draw a sad face if the people have more selfish motivations.

1. Megan decides to go on the youth-group service project because she thinks it will be fun to spend time with her two good friends that day.

2. Elke offers to feed her elderly neighbor's cat while the neighbor visits her out-of-town grandchildren. Elke offers because she knows that her neighbor cannot afford to put Kitty in a kennel.

3. Travis likes to assist in the preschool Sunday school class because he enjoys the little kids and knows the teacher needs an extra person's help.

4. Sureen helps a classmate on crutches carry books between classes, even though she does not know this student very well. She just does not want to see the classmate struggle.

5. Ayake makes sure she helps the teachers before and after school whenever her grades are borderline. She helps them in hopes of getting some extra credit.

6. David knows he could win a prize if he completes a checklist of service projects, so he works hard at doing projects.

7. Kara looks for little things she can do for her family and teachers. She tries to make sure that they do not find out who helped them, keeping it a secret between her and Jesus.

The book of 1 Peter talks about ways to serve that honor God. Read the verses to find key ideas about serving others. Solve the code by looking at the green letters that represent a letter in black. Fill in the missing letter by looking throughout the puzzle for a word in black that has that green letter represented in the word. For example, in Exercise 8, u-h-l-k equals **h-a-v-e**, so u equals **h** and so on. So wherever you see a green u, fill in an **h** on the above line. (Note: Not all green letters match a black letter.)

8. Have ___ ___ ___ ___ ___ ___ ___ ___ ___ ___. (1 Peter 3:8)

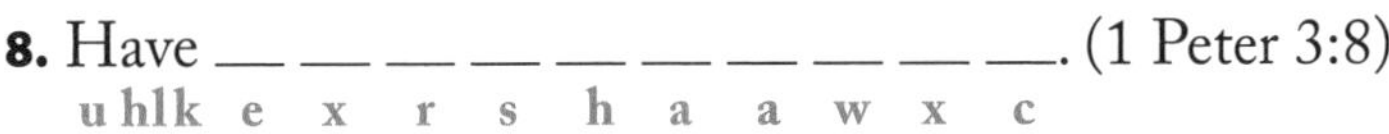

uhlk e x r s h a a w x c

9. Keep a ___ ___ ___ ___ ___ ___ ___ ___ ___ ___ ___ ___ ___ ___ ___. (1 Peter 3:16)

t kks h e n k h g e x c a e w k c e k

10. Love each other. (1 Peter 4:8)

n x lk kheu xju kg

11. Serve with ___ ___ ___’___ ___ ___ ___ ___ ___ ___ ___ ___. (1 Peter 4:11)

akglk fwju o x q ’ a a j g k c o j u

12. ___ ___ ___ ___ ___ ___ ___ when you suffer for Jesus. (1 Peter 4:13)

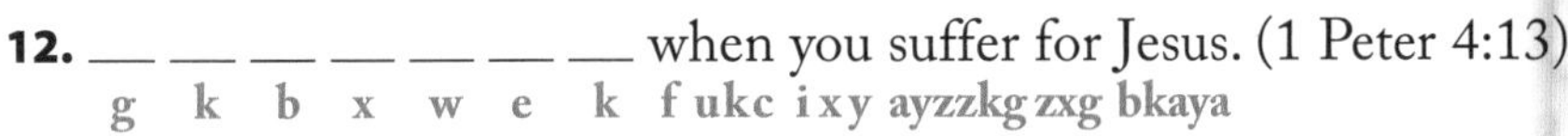

g k b x w e k f ukc ixy ayzzkg zxg bkaya

13. Be ___ ___ ___ ___ ___ ___, and God will give you grace. (1 Peter 5:5)

mk u y r m n k hcq oxq fwnnowlk ixy oghek

31.4 1–2 Peter: Service and Growth

1. Remember that God's children are chosen, royal, holy, and special (1 Peter 2:9). God provides everything that His children need to live holy lives. Read 2 Peter 1:3–4 and fill in the blanks.

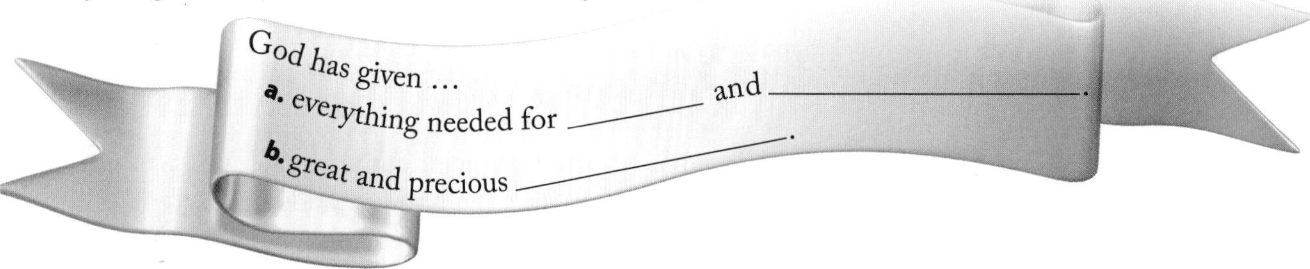

God has given ...
a. everything needed for ________ and ________.
b. great and precious ________.

2. Write on the lines the eight characteristics from 2 Peter 1:5–7 that Christians should diligently make every effort to grow in.

________ ________ ________ ________

________ ________ ________ ________

Read 2 Peter 3:10–14. Circle all the right answers. Then follow the directions for Exercise 7.

3. What is the special day that will fulfill the salvation of Christians and take them home?
a. the day of the Lord **b.** the day of Jubilee **c.** the day of Pentecost

4. What will be made new when the Lord returns?
a. the Old and New Testaments **b.** the heavens and the earth **c.** the thieves in the night

5. What will be a part of these things or people (from Exercise 4's answer) that will have been made new?
a. saints and sinners together **b.** getting everything I want for selfish motives **c.** righteousness and no evil

6. What should Christians do while waiting for Christ's return?
a. live holy and effective lives **b.** look forward to heaven **c.** be at peace in Jesus

7. Choose one of the characteristics from Exercise 2. On another paper, draw a picture to show how that characteristic could help a Christian while he or she waits for the Lord's return.

Name ________________________________

1–3 John and Jude: Love and Truth 32.1

1. Fellowship is a central theme in 1 John. The basis for fellowship is found in 1 John 1:1–2:23. Some parts of the outline have been completed for you. Skim the references and then choose the phrase from the Outline Bank that best summarizes the verses. Use each phrase only once.

Outline Bank

- confess sin
- love the world
- love one another
- obey God's commands
- antichrist
- walk in the light

I. The Basis for Fellowship (1:1–2:23)

A. Introduction (1:1–4)
  1. Eyewitness to the Word of Life (1:1–2)
  2. Fellowship with God and one another (1:3–4)

B. Signs of being in fellowship (1:5–2:14)
  1. ______________________________ (1:5–7)
  2. ______________________________ (1:8–10)
  3. ______________________________ (2:3–4)
  4. ______________________________ (2:9–10)

C. Cautions of fellowship (2:15–23)
  1. Do not ______________________________ (2:15)
  2. Do not believe any ______________________________ (2:22–23)

2. Children of God walk in fellowship with God by loving, obeying, and staying pure. Read the references below and write in each row the action believers should take (or not take). Then give yourself a checkup by coloring the lightbulb in the column that best describes your response to that action (or lack of action). Note that all references are from 1 John.

A Christian should ...	Yes	No	Sometimes
1:9			
2:3			
2:10			
2:15			
3:3			
3:6			
3:18			

32.2 1–3 John and Jude: Love and Truth

1. The behavior of fellowship is found in 1 John 2:24–5:21. Continue the outline of 1 John that was started in the previous lesson. Skim the references and then choose the phrase from the Outline Bank that best summarizes the verses. Use each phrase only once.

II. The Behavior of Fellowship (2:24–5:21)

Outline Bank
assurance of salvation
have no fear
guidance in prayer
love like Christ
practice righteousness
knowing God
live a pure life
abide or remain in Christ
victory over the world
know the Spirit of Truth

A. Characteristics of fellowship (2:24–5:3)

1. ______________________ (2:24–25)
2. ______________________ (3:3)
3. ______________________ (3:7)
4. ______________________ (3:16)
5. ______________________ (4:6)
6. ______________________ (4:18)

B. Benefits of fellowship (5:4–21)

1. ______________________ (5:4–5)
2. ______________________ (5:11–13)
3. ______________________ (5:14–15)
4. ______________________ (5:20)

2. As you read through the book of 1 John, you may have noticed that it sounds like an instruction manual. List the five steps for remaining in Christ that are found in 1 John.

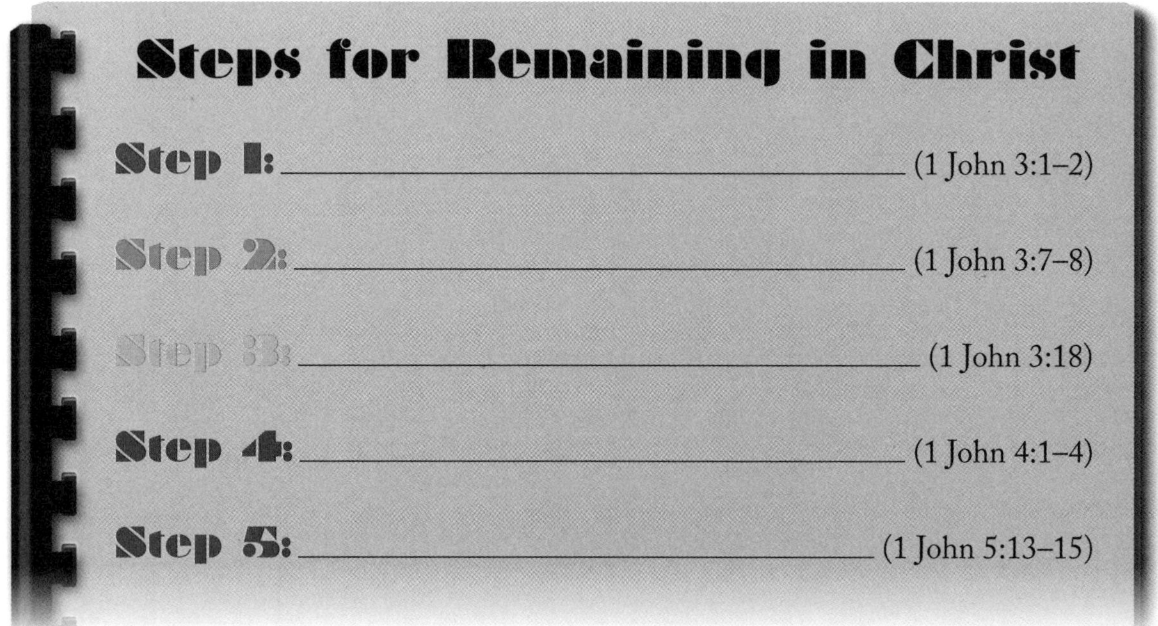

Steps for Remaining in Christ

Step 1: ______________________ (1 John 3:1–2)

Step 2: ______________________ (1 John 3:7–8)

Step 3: ______________________ (1 John 3:18)

Step 4: ______________________ (1 John 4:1–4)

Step 5: ______________________ (1 John 5:13–15)

3. Define propitiation. ______________________

Name ____

1–3 John and Jude: Love and Truth

32.3

In 3 John 11–12, John gave another example of someone, besides Gaius, who walked in truth and love. Use the code to fill in the blanks to show ways that Demetrius showed faithfulness and goodness.

1. ___ _ ________ ______

2. ___ ___ _______ ____ ___ ____

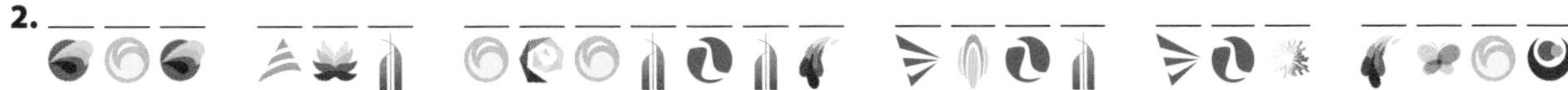

3. ___ ____ ___ ____

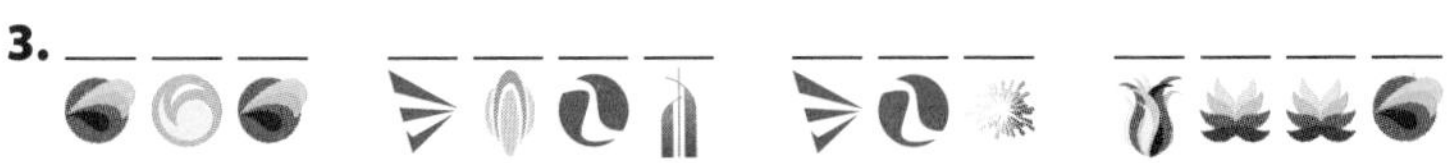

4. ______ __ ________ ___

5. _________ _ ____ ________

a =	h =	r =
b =	i =	s =
c =	l =	t =
d =	m =	v =
e =	n =	w =
f =	o =	x =
g =	p =	y =

God does not want His followers to exhibit the characteristics of Diotrephes (3 John 9–10). Rather, He wants His followers to be full of faithfulness, goodness, and love. The themes John presented over and over again are love and truth. Explain what you can do to show God's love and truth to ...

6. someone who has gossiped about you: ______________________________

7. someone who seems to reject your friendship: ______________________________

8. *someone whom others make fun of:* ______________________________

9. someone who is always getting you in trouble: ______________________________

10. someone who makes fun of you: ______________________________

11. *someone who is always grumbling and complaining:* ______________________________

32.4 1–3 John and Jude: Love and Truth

Read the scenarios. Circle the letter of the advice that you think Jude would have agreed with the most.

1. Blake found at his new school a group of students who are friendly but who do not believe in Jesus. He wants to be their friend because they have a lot of fun. What should he do?
   a. Blake should talk to them and be nice to them, but also be cautious of becoming like them.
   b. Blake should avoid them.
   c. Blake should hang out with them and do what they do.

2. Miranda is pretty, wealthy, and popular. She is also very conceited, negative, and mean. Miranda constantly picks on Tasha because Tasha is different. It makes Tasha mad. She wants to get back at Miranda and hurt Miranda as she has been hurt. What should Tasha do?
   a. She should privately get back at Miranda.
   b. She should publicly humiliate Miranda.
   c. She should pray for Miranda, trusting that God will take care of the whole situation.
   d. She should ignore Miranda and pretend that nothing bad has ever happened.

3. Mark wants to grow closer to God. What godly disciplines will help him?
   a. He should build himself up in the faith.
   b. He should pray in the Holy Spirit.
   c. Mark should remember God's love.
   d. He should cautiously show mercy to people who are sinning.
   e. He should do all of the above.

Answer the questions.

4. Read Jude 3. What strong command did Jude give his audience?

____

5. How could you respond to Jude's command in your life?

____

____

Name ______________________________

Revelation: Future Events 33.1

1. Complete a report card of the seven churches evaluated in Revelation 2–3. Mark whether they passed or failed on the basis of their attribute and write suggestions for improvement for those that failed.

REPORT CARD

Church	Attribute	Pass	Fail
Ephesus	loveless	☐	☐
Smyrna	persecuted	☐	☐
Pergamum	worldly	☐	☐
Thyratira	corrupt	☐	☐
Sardis	dead	☐	☐
Philadelphia	faithful	☐	☐
Laodicea	lukewarm	☐	☐

Suggestions: ______________________________

____

____

____

____

2. Evaluate your relationship with the Lord. Then write a short prayer expressing a desire to follow Him more closely (or expressing anything else you would like to say to Him).

____

____

____

3. John had a revelation of end times. Fill in the names of Jesus found in the book of Revelation.

a. Revelation 1:8 _ _ _ _ _ _ _ _ _ _ _ _ _

b. Revelation 3:14 _ _ _ _

c. Revelation 5:5 _ _ _ _

d. Revelation 5:6 _ _ _ _

e. Revelation 15:3 _ _ _ _ _ _ _ _ _ _ _ _ _ _ _ _

f. Revelation 19:13 _ _ _ _ _ _ _ _ _

g. Revelation 22:16 _ _ _ _ _ _ _ _ _ _ _ _ _ _ _ _ _ _ _ _ _

33.2 Revelation: Future Events

The vision of heaven John had was almost beyond his ability to describe. He was limited in words to describe scenes never seen on the earth. Read the Scriptures and match them with their correct description.

1. Revelation 4:3 •

2. Revelation 4:4 •

3. Revelation 4:5 •

4. Revelation 4:6a •

5. Revelation 4:6b–8 •

6. Revelation 4:9–11 •

- • the 24 elders bowing and casting their crowns before the throne as they give glory, honor, and praise to the Lord
- • lightning, thunder, and voices coming from the throne and seven lamps of fire burning before the throne
- • 24 thrones (around God's throne) where 24 elders are sitting in white robes and wearing gold crowns on their heads
- • a sea of glass in front of the throne
- • God's throne with a rainbow around it
- • four living creatures who are full of eyes, who have six wings, and who are situated around the throne

Answer the question and follow the directions.

7. What impression did John have about the one who sits on the throne?

____

8. Choose one feature of heaven's throne that John described. Explain why it impresses or intrigues you and why you would like to see that part of the throne scene.

____

____

9. Revelation 5:8 indicates that God saves believers' prayers in golden bowls in heaven. The verse describes these prayers as incense presented to the Lamb. Write a prayer to add to the golden bowls in heaven.

Name ______________________________

Revelation: Future Events 33.3

Refer to Revelation 19:11–16 to find details about the white horse and its rider.

1. Draw the details of the rider on the picture.

2. Write the rider's three names that are mentioned in verses 11, 13, and 16.

____

Read Revelation 20:11–15. Circle the correct choice to make true statements about the final judgment.

3. The great white throne of judgment is for (unbelievers / believers).

4. The names of believers in Christ are written in the (Bible / Book of Life).

5. The other books mentioned in the passage list the (actions of unbelievers / church attendance of believers).

6. (Rewards / Punishments) are given at this judgment.

7. The dead (stay in Hades or hell / come out of the sea, death, and Hades) for this judgment.

8. At this judgment, (Satan and unbelievers are cast into the lake of fire / people choose to follow Jesus).

33.4 Revelation: Future Events

The first and last books of the Bible tell the beginning and end of God's big-picture narrative. Genesis 15:3 foretells the coming Savior. The New Testament records Jesus' life, death, resurrection, and return. Jesus fulfills God's plan of redemption. Complete the chart by writing each ending found in Revelation.

Genesis	Revelation
1. God created the world.	Revelation 21:1 ______________________
2. Satan introduced sin into the world.	Revelation 20:10 ______________________
3. Humans fell into sin and under sin's curse.	Revelation 22:3 ______________________
4. All people were separated from God.	Revelation 22:5 ______________________
5. Tears and sorrow became part of life.	Revelation 21:4 ______________________
6. The Tree of Life became unavailable to people on the earth.	Revelation 21:10 and 22:2 ______________________
7. Death entered the world.	Revelation 20:14 ______________________
8. People scattered all around the world and spoke various languages.	Revelation 7:9–10 ______________________

9. Fill in the time line of events recorded in the book of Revelation. Write the correct letter in each of the colored circles to put the events in order.

a. bowl judgments
b. John's letters to the seven churches
c. Satan and unbelievers being cast into the lake of fire
d. John's glimpse into heaven
e. new heaven and new earth
f. great white throne of judgment
g. trumpet judgments
h. white horse and its rider
i. seal judgments

○ ○ ○ ○ ○ ○ ○ ○ ○ → Eternity

Name ______________________________

Review 34.1

Matthew recorded Jesus' Sermon on the Mount that taught about living in God's kingdom—a direct contrast to the values taught by the world. Follow the directions and answer the question.

1. Read Matthew 5:43–44 and match the phrases.

world's values •
Kingdom's values •

• love only your neighbor
• love your enemies
• hate your enemies
• pray for those who persecute you

2. How have you shown Kingdom values in your life?

____

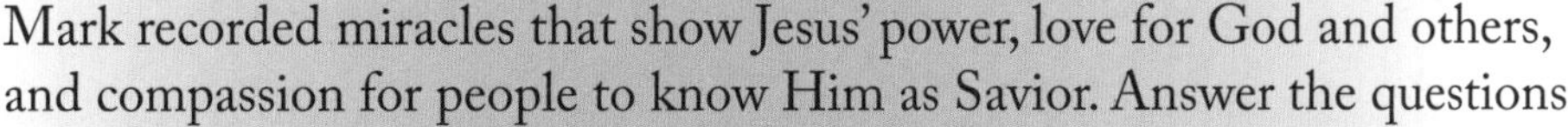

Mark recorded miracles that show Jesus' power, love for God and others, and compassion for people to know Him as Savior. Answer the questions.

3. After calming a storm, how did Jesus' disciples respond? (Mark 4:41)

____

4. After Jesus healed a deaf and mute man, how did His followers respond? (Mark 7:37)

____

5. How has your faith grown this year?

____

Luke recorded many of Jesus' parables. Look up the verses and fill in each answer by drawing a picture. Then answer the question.

6. The parables of the lost ________ (Luke 15:4), the lost ________ (Luke 15:8), and the lost ________ (Luke 15:13) show Jesus' concern to ________ (Luke 19:10) and to save the lost.

7. How have you shown compassion, kindness, and forgiveness this school year?

____

John recorded Jesus' teachings about the Holy Spirit. Look up these Scriptures in which Jesus is talking about the Holy Spirit. Circle the answer that correctly completes the sentences and answers the question.

8. The Holy Spirit indwells, or lives in, (only religious leaders / all believers). (John 14:16)

9. The Holy Spirit convicts people of (sin / being a Christian). (John 16:8)

10. The Holy Spirit guides believers into (all truth / all religions). (John 16:13)

11. How has the Holy Spirit affected your life this year?

____

34.2 Review

1. Match the phrases beneath the Time Line to the corresponding event on the Time Line. On the lines near each matching Time Line event, write the correct alphabet letter of the phrases.

a. Christ's return to heaven, which showed God's omnipotence
b. the fulfillment of Old Testament prophecies about the Messiah
c. a transforming and dramatic encounter with Jesus
d. victory over sin and gift of salvation
e. God's gift of the Holy Spirit to indwell believers, salvation of people, discipling of believers, and establishment of local churches
f. cause of the scattering of persecuted believers and the spread of the gospel
g. public display of commitment to God

Read these Scriptures: Romans 5:18, 5:20, and 12:1–2; and 2 Corinthians 5:18–21. Fill in the blanks with a word from the Word Bank.

Word Bank

giving
transform
grace
unity
reconciliation
conform
morally
justifies
demonstrate

2. In Romans, Paul examined that ______________ gives victory over sin, God's righteousness ______________ believers, God's love can ______________ Christians into Christ's image when they ______________ to line up with God's Word.

3. In Corinthians, Paul instructed believers to live ______________ and in ______________, to ______________ love to others, to practice ______________, and to share the ministry of ______________.

Name ______________________________

Review 34.3

The books in the Bible are not arranged chronologically. Listed below are the presumed years when the New Testament epistles and book of prophecy were written. Fill in the name of these New Testament books. (Some letters have been provided as a hint.) Then follow the directions in Exercise 17.

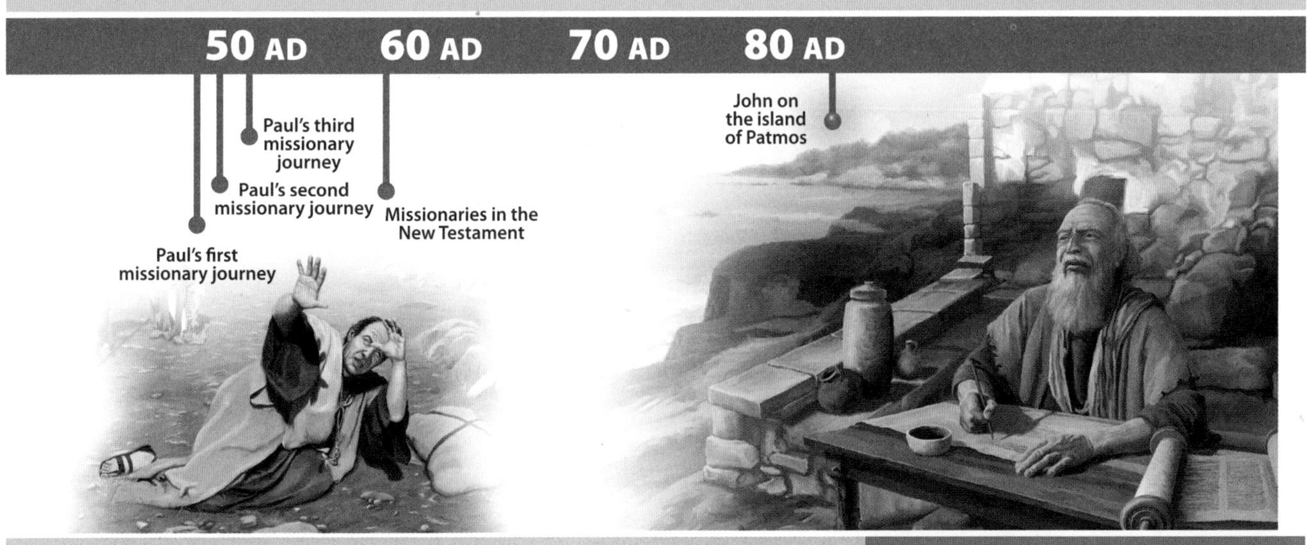

1. __ a __ __ __ 48 AD
2. 1–2 __ __ __ __ __ __ __ __ __ __ __ __ __ 49–54 AD
3. __ a __ __ __ __ __ __ __ 50–55 AD
4. 1–2 __ __ __ __ __ __ __ __ __ __ __ 56 AD
5. __ __ __ __ __ __ 57 AD
6. __ __ __ __ __ __ __ __ 60 AD
7. __ __ __ __ __ __ __ __ __ 60–64 AD
8. __ __ __ __ __ __ __ __ __ __ __ 60–64 AD
9. __ o __ __ __ __ __ __ __ __ 60–64 AD
10. __ __ __ __ __ __ __ 60–69 AD
11. __ __ __ __ 60–95 AD
12. __ __ __ __ __ 64 AD
13. 1–2 __ __ __ __ __ __ __ 64–67 AD
14. 1–2 __ __ __ __ __ 64–70 AD
15. __ __ __ __ __ __ __ __ __ __ 69–96 AD
16. 1–3 __ __ __ __ 80–95 AD

17. Choose one of the New Testament books listed above and write about how it has influenced your life.

____
____
____
____
____
____
____
____
____
____
____

34.4 Review

1. Write the number of the definitions on the lines next to the matching Glossary word in the box. Check your answers by adding the numbers in each column. If answers are correct, the sum for each row, column, and corner-to-corner diagonal will match. Write that sum on the line to complete the sentence.

1 the promises from God that involved animal sacrifices and obedience from people
2 the promise of God fulfilled through the sacrifice of Jesus and accepted by people through faith in Him
3 knowing Christ and following Him through consistent obedience, faithful service, and mature growth
4 share the gospel with others
5 the cruel treatment of someone because of the person's beliefs
6 the time when a person decides to follow Jesus
7 the process of being set apart for a specific, holy purpose
8 become like another in form or character
9 change into something new
10 the act of being brought back into relationship
11 Jewish and Gentile believers together making up the Church, the Body of Christ
12 living for God by living a life to help others
13 the event when Jesus returns to the earth
14 the act of returning something to its original condition
15 the continued effort to stay on task or hold to a belief when encountering difficulty
16 an external or internal attempt to get someone to do something wrong

__ Old Covenant	__ perseverance	__ restoration	__ evangelize
__ servanthood	__ conversion	__ sanctification	__ transform
__ conform	__ reconciliation	__ mystery of Christ	__ persecution
__ second coming of Christ	__ biblical success	__ New Covenant	__ temptation

THE sum is ____.

2. Choose one of the Glossary words and explain how it applies to your life.

____

____

Glossary

agape selfless love

ambassador someone sent as an official representative or messenger

antichrist one who denies God the Father and God the Son

apostasy the abandonment of faith in Jesus as Savior and Lord

apostle someone God sent to share the gospel and strengthen the Church

authority the power and right to give orders or enforce rules

biblical success knowing Christ and following Him through consistent obedience, faithful service, and mature growth

bondage the state of being a slave

character the core of who someone is even when no one is looking

commitment a promise to be dedicated to someone or something

conform become like another in form or character

contentment being satisfied with one's situation

conversion the time when a person decides to follow Jesus

convict to convince of error or sin

covenant a promise or agreement between two people or groups

denying oneself putting one's own desires aside to follow God's will

doctrine the basic teachings of the Christian faith based on the Bible

dwell live in a particular place

end times the events leading up to Christ's return and culminating with God's final judgment of sin

epistle letter

evangelist someone who shares the gospel with others

evangelize to share the gospel with others

favoritism unfairly treating a person or group better than others

freedom the state of not being a slave

Gentile a non-Jewish person

Incarnation the truth that the Son of God became human

indwelling living in

Glossary

joy a lasting state of great delight or satisfaction

justify to declare righteous

kingdom of heaven the reign of God, both present and future

lifestyle the usual way of life that reflects an individual's values

mandate a command or an order given

meta beyond or complete

mind of Christ thinking like Christ

mystery of Christ Jewish and Gentile believers together making up the Church, the Body of Christ

narrative a story

New Covenant the promise of God fulfilled through the sacrifice of Jesus and accepted by people through faith in Him

Old Covenant the promises from God that involved animal sacrifices and obedience from people

persecution the cruel treatment of someone because of the person's beliefs

perseverance the continued effort to stay with a task or hold to a belief even when encountering difficulty

phileo brotherly love or friendship

propitiation a sacrifice that satisfies completely

purity the state of being free from contamination

reconciliation the act of being brought back into relationship

restoration the act of returning something to its original condition

sanctification the process of being set apart for a specific, holy purpose

second coming of Christ the event when Jesus returns to the earth

servanthood living for God by living a life to help others

slave a person who is owned by someone else and has to do what the owner says

sojourner someone who stops temporarily to live somewhere

Son of Man a title that refers to Jesus as fully human

spiritual readiness being strong in the Lord and thereby being able to resist evil

superior more excellent

temptation an external or internal attempt to get someone to do something wrong

theology the study of God

transform change into something new

trial a hard or troubling time or situation

value something of great worth or importance that influences decisions

wretched miserable or shameful in defeat

Bible Journal

Bible Journal

Bible Journal

Bible Journal

Bible Journal

Bible Journal

Bible Journal

Bible Journal

Bible Journal

Bible Journal

Bible Journal

Bible Journal

Bible Journal

Bible Journal

Bible Journal

Bible Journal